A Toy Truck For A Marine

And Other Christmas Tales

From
A Simple Missionary Priest

trimarkpress

Published by TriMark Press, Inc., Deerfield Beach, florida.

Library of Congress Cataloging-in-Publication Data

A Toy Truck For A Marine
And Other Christmas Tales
From A Simple Missionary Priest
Illustrations By Chad Thompson
p. cm.
ISBN: 978-1-943401-80-2
Library of Congress Control Number: 2020919403
J-20
10 9 8 7 6 5 4 3 2 1
First Edition
Printed and Bound in the United States of America

A Publication of TriMark Press, Inc.
1525 NW 3rd Street, Suite 10
Deerfield Beach, FL. 33442
800-889-0693

Welcome to Mikey's Christmas!

Introduction

Also known as Mikey and Miguel, Miguelito doesn't have a last name *and*, like Christmas and Santa Claus, he's ageless. Depending on the story, Mikey ranges in age from early grade school to young adult. His circle of friends includes residents of Little Havana, priests, addicts and Marines just returning home from combat.

More importantly, however, Mikey has a unique ability to express the meaning of Christmas and the essence of the Christian Mystery honestly and straightforwardly. The Christmas stories of Miguelito are among a collection of sermons or homilies prepared by a Miami-based priest and missioner as his annual "Christmas gift" to his family and friends.

Many of these stories begin with a brief "introduction" for those who gather each year for Christmas Eve Mass at his family's home.

We have been able to recall the years for many stories, others are known but to God.

While originally written to be read aloud, the author describes them as "oral, lyric prose" and designed to offer an opportunity for quiet meditation on the Gift of Christmas.

Proceeds from *A Toy Truck for a Marine* will be used to support the Maryknoll Sisters Contemplative Community – "the Cloister" or "the Chalet" – and the author's ministries of drug addictions counseling in South Florida..

2006

Of Giraffes and Blue Jeans
and Talking Parrots

Have you ever wondered about God?

I don't mean prayed. Or even thought about God the way that theologians do with their strangely abstract ideas such as how many angels can dance on the head of a pin. But wondered – jumped into the awe and mystery of God, trying to sort Him out and make sense of God.

(Oh, and you'll pardon me, please, if I can Him "Him," but that's the way it turns out – when I begin to wonder about God.)

The ancient Jews of the time of our first Christmas wondered about God. Wondering, you see, is very important. When you think... Well, thinking is just plain thinking. It really does not change you very much. But wondering... When you wonder you try to explore – to know, to come more and more deeply in touch, in tune, to feel with – what you are wondering about. Wondering, really wondering is part of falling in love.

And so, ancient Jews used to wonder about God – just so they could love Him more.

They wondered about time for God, and decided that there was no past and there will be no future for God – that everything is now. Isn't that a great idea? It means that if you don't like what is happening now, you can go to another now that seems to suit you better. Just think about it: All the bad times are forever, but so are all the good times, too.

And, we are told, they wondered about why God created us. It was, they realized, because He – God – was so lonely. It must have been difficult to be God before He made us. All alone up there – out there, wherever – without anyone to talk to or laugh with.

As I thought about all of this, I began to wonder about God and Christmas and Creation.

I got to thinking about just how hard it must be for God for Christmas to be all the time, and to wondering about what He did for Christmas presents. I mean, just the hours that He had to spend shopping and wrapping would probably keep a couple of lesser gods busy full time.

(I'll bet my sister and my mother really like this idea of God – always shopping. Why, there's a God after their hearts.)

But think about it. Our first Christmas had already been happening for centuries of centuries for God when it finally happened for us.

Imagine the shopping lists that God has to go through. Of course, the first Christmas was easy. After all, your own private star.

From that point on, however, things began to get complicated – even for God. And so there came talking birds that laugh and sing and call their owners by name, so that the Christ Child might learn all the better to speak. For, if one day He was going to teach "Blessed are the peace makers for they shall be called the children of God" and "Blessed are the merciful...," He had better learn to speak at an early age.

And candied apples. You mean you didn't know? Yes – God. He thought candied apples would be a great idea for the Child's sixth birthday in our time. After all, the apple had had such a bad rap up to that point. Besides, the year before God invented oranges all juicy and sticky and wondrous to peel and squeeze on a fall afternoon as boys played on the hillsides of Galilee. So the candied apple seemed like an all-round good idea for our Christmas number six.

And mangoes. Truth is that with mangoes God figured He had scored so well that He actually considered mangoes a century's worth of gifts. Besides, the best mangoes of all are beautifully golden.

One of my favorites was the Christmas when God got God-time and Man-time all mixed-up, and thinking somehow the soon-to-be 14 years-old Jesus could use some new clothes for His birthday (parents always want to give teenagers clothes for birthdays, even when they're God), the Father made old, well-worn, comfortable blue jeans and Topsiders.

There were other Christmases in God's time and in ours – each with special gifts. Gifts given to His Son, our brother. Gifts given to lift the burden of God's loneliness, to fill the heart of a child born in a stable and grown to manhood as a teacher and a friend.

Why, one year the Father suddenly realized that while summer afternoons spent swimming with friends were fun and laughter-filled, how much better they might be if there were *just something more*. And so, for a very special Christmas, on the eighth day, God created tropical fish – parrot and clown and zebra fish, fish of every design imaginable, small and large, quick and slow – and tropical reefs with coral and color. And God saw that it was very good.

Oh, yes and laughter, and the light in children's eyes, the candle's flicker on the cheeks of your lover, the gentleness of a touch, and the words "I love you."

You mean you did not know? Why, of course. They're all Christmas gifts – some given in God-time and some in our time.

Please do not think my wonderings to be strange. After all, isn't God our Father, as well as the Heavenly Father of the Child whose birth we celebrate this night? And doesn't He wish us only that which is good?

You see, in reality our God is a God – a Father – of little gifts. Of course, there was the Star. But ever since, well maybe except for elephants and giraffes, He has always been a God of little gifts. Little gifts and Christmas.

Why Christmas? Because God has always wanted to be Father. And talking birds and coral reefs, candied apples and comfortable, old, torn blue jeans stained by the run off of juicy oranges and mangoes — these are all His little gifts.

Gifts made real for the Son whom He, this night, gives to us; gifts made real for us because His son has come this night, born in a stable, as Brother and Lord, Prince of Peace, and Wonder Counselor.

You see, when we begin to understand God as Father and the Giver of Little Gifts, all of life becomes Christmas — every hour, day and moment. And all life offers — stubbed toes, toothaches, cauliflower and Brussels sprouts, button down shirts, and Hurricane football games, tears and laughter, families and friends, pain and sorrows, joys and hopes, birth and death and Resurrection. All become the Little Gifts of the Christmas of the present moment.

At least that's the way it seems to me — when I wonder about God and time and creation and Christmas.

Please enjoy this collection of "little gifts."

Merry Christmas

The Mikey Stories

2013

$\mathcal{A}$ Christmas Truck for A Marine ...

Over half a century and three-and-something generations, the family grew and spread from *La Pequena Havana* – Little Havana – and Hialeah to Westchester, Kendal, Pinecrest, and even Weston.

As generations took root like an ever-spreading banyan tree, no one enjoyed it more than the family's youngest member, whom some were considering nominating for to Ripley's Believe-It-Or-Not as the kid with the most uncles in the world. There were doctor and dentist uncles, mechanic and lawyer uncles, teacher and business uncles, banker uncles and every possible kind of sales person uncle. And, if the family tree didn't cover a profession or need, the adoption of aunts and uncles would fill the void. There's an almost unlimited number of advantages to being part of a family with so many *tios* and *tias, primos* and *primas* – uncles and aunts and cousins, both boys and girls. You never have to worry about getting really sick – the doctors make house calls. Everybody's car runs very, very smoothly. And whatever the sport, there's an uncle or cousin who's ready to join *Papi* in his role as a great coach or personal trainer.

Of course, in the providence of God, there has to be some balance for all those benefits and that was the simple fact that Miguelito couldn't get away with anything without *Mami* and *Papi* knowing in real time thanks to the Cuban Internet.

There was, of course, in the totally incomprehensible universe that is called *Miguelitolandia* — Mikey Land to those who do not speak Spanglish — a certain unwritten, indeed unspoken, and to all the world except Mikey, incomprehensible logic for *tio-razco* — unclehood. First, female cousins, no matter what their age and unless they were married to a tio, were primas — cousins. Males, however, were primos only if they were Mikey-size. And, since he was the last of all the grandchildren, at least according to the unanimous chorus of his aunts, almost every male fell into the uncle category. If you were more than a head-and-a-half-taller and/or sported a beard that required shaving more than twice a month, you were definitely a tio. Which, in the world according to Mikey, meant that every male relative was officially an uncle. And, if you were a tio's best friend, essentially grew up in or ate pots-full of *arroz con pollo* or *frijoles negros* — chicken and rise or black beans — in Mikey's or the *abuelos'* — grandparents' — home, you were an officially unofficially adopted tio.

So it was that when Mikey's student-at-the-University-of-Miami Uncle Nick caused something of a seismic shock of earth quake magnitude by announcing that he was — horror-of-horrors — moving into the Sigma Chi Fraternity house on campus, the family processioned (is that a word?) to the house and established Nick — and by extension Mikey — in a wonderland of uncles. And Mikey never missed a beat; he memorized the route and, essentially, considered the house as his own domain. Pledges — Mikey didn't quite understand that concept — were assigned as MDs — Mikey Drivers after dark. He was honorary coach to every intramural team and his homework was checked and rechecked by students who would eventually graduate with honors and highest honors and some whose parents would simply be happy to see them graduate. No wonder that, with sixty uncles overlooking every assignment, he shot to the head of his class.

And, best of all, he always had at least sixty — sometimes as many as 80 and 90 tios because every graduating class was replaced by new and more amazing groups of pledges and brothers.

In truth, it was difficult to tell who was more fond of whom — Mikey of his tios or the tios of Mikey. But one thing was certain: There was no tio like Tio Connor. "He's really, really nice; he tells jokes, he's wants to be a children's doctor; he's got a great — I mean a really great — car that he bought for himself; he has blonde hair and he smiles more than anyone else in the whole world — the biggest smile you have ever seen," he excitedly told Mami and Papi and los abuelos over dinner. "And he's got all kinds of tattoos..." (At this news Abuela nearly choked on her own flan and Mami thought she might be needing to go to bed *con un dolor de cabeza bien fuerte* – with a really bad headache). "They're the names of some of his friends who died, and... And, and...He calls me Dude, and Duster, and Duderoo.... And, and...." His thoughts were racing so fast his tongue couldn't catch-up.

"And he's a MARINE."

With one word, tumbling off Mikey's tongue, Connor was transformed. *"Pues,"* announced Abuelo, *"es familia* – well, he's family." The matter was settled. Tattoos, until that moment *verboten* (if I can mix languages,) in la familia, were suddenly – well, not quite acceptable – but acceptable on Connor because *"si pues, es un Marine."*

It seemed, to la familia, that the world – or at least Mikey's world – had changed from heliocentric, moving around the sun, to Connor-centric. And, while Papi was once able to stop Mikey dead in his tracks *con una mirada* – with a look – now he was controlled with a simple promise (never threats, I don't believe in threatening kids; but I'm great at promises) like "I'm going to tell Connor" or, even worse, "You won't be able to go with Connor." Such promises could affect nearly miraculous transformations.

When it became clear that Connor was going to stay at the fraternity house during the week-long Thanksgiving break, it was equally clear that Mikey's sun would be given no choice: He would join his huge Cuban-American-Miami family for Thanksgiving dinner.

The quintessential American holiday was organized bedlam. With so many coming and going and eating and three languages filling the air — hey, we're in Miami, of course three languages: English, Spanish and Spanglish — Connor thought that actual battle was more organized. As the sun set and Papi began nodding off on the sofa, Connor gave Mikey a subtle but familiar jerk of the head that Miguelito had come to recognize as a silent expression of "Let's blow this firetrap" — a classic Connor-ism. "Hey, Dudester," he said. "There's no school tomorrow. How'd you like to hit up Toys-R-Us? I've got more than a thousand bucks burning a hole in my pocket for Toys-For-Tots; it's a Marine project."

A project for THE MARINES! Even if they had wanted to, Mami and Papi and los abuelos could not say No to THE MARINES. But, insisted Abuela, Connor could not leave without something approximating twenty pounds of *arroz, frijoles negros, pavo, platanos maduro* — rice, black beans, turkey, fried bananas, and enough of Abuela's flan to stop the hearts of an entire Marine battalion — "*por si acaso* – in case you are hungry later."

For the next few weeks, Connor and the Dudester and the rest of the Sigma Chis, brothers and pledges, and sorority girls galore, became an extension of Toys-For-

Tots and THE MARINES. Car washes, toy collections, car hold-ups for cash on US1. Connor wasn't just any Marine — he was Secretaries of the Navy and Defense all rolled into one. And when not in school or sleeping, Tio and the Dudester were shopping, selecting, wrapping, name-tagging, and planning deliveries.

On the last Friday afternoon of the semester, Tios Nick and Connor managed to con, cajole and just generally overwhelm Mami and Papi with an idea: Mikey would spend the weekend at the fraternity house. He'd go to bed early, study, and help wrap gifts and attend Saturday's fraternity Christmas party. And they promised that he'd be home safe and sound on Sunday. The look on Mami's and Papi's faces was as if it had been proposed that they move to Alaska. But then came the clincher: All Connor's Marine friends were going to be the guests of honor. THE MARINES. What parent — in fact, what Cuban-American parent — could say no to that?

It was a kid's Dream of a Life Time. A Sigma Chi Party. So many beautiful young women all dressed-up and they all kissed him. On the dance floor he did his Cuban heritage proud. Connor's Marine friends saluted and brothers high-fived him. And, Mikey smiled so much that, when he finally unrolled his sleeping bag on Tio Connor's floor, he actually complained that his jaw hurt.

"What a night, Dudester," Connor sighed, falling

— I mean falling — onto his bed. "So great to see those guys laughin' and smilin'. For some of them, this was probably the first time they've had so much fun in years. They've seen so much war and pain and some of them are still so afraid that they actually sleep with their guns right next to them in bed. The closest they come to being kids is this toys thing — and then they're actually letting other kids be kids." And with that, Connor drifted off.

But Miguelito fell asleep and dreamed and woke to those words: "They've seen so much war and pain and they're still so afraid...."

As promised, Connor delivered Miguelito home right on time for Sunday afternoon Mass, parting, as always, *con un abrazo fuerte* — with a big hug. For Miguelito, however, those words — "They've seen so much war and pain and they're still afraid..." — continued to run through his head like an evil ghost of Christmas past. At home, Papi could stand — would stand — his silence no longer. "Miguel, don't tell me 'nothing.' I know something's wrong. What's happened?"

"Papi," said Miguelito, "My truck collection. Is it really mine?"

"Chico, how many times have you heard the story. When Abuelo first arrived in America, before he even knew Abuela, he worked in a gas station — his first job — and bought three toy trucks at Christmas for the sons and grandsons he planned someday would be his. Every year since then, he's bought three trucks — one for me, one for you to play with and one for the collection, never opened, always saved. Abuelo always says they're a down payment on your college tuition."

"But, Papi. Is it MY collection or Abuelo's?"

"Of course, *Hijo*. It's yours. *Porque?*"

In seconds Mikey told the entire story — Toys-For-Tots, Tio's Marine friends, but most importantly that he couldn't forget Tio's words — "They've seen so much war and pain and they're still so afraid...."

"Papi," said Miguelito, "I want to give my collection to Marines... "

It was done, settled, *se acabo la cosa*. Mikey had made up his mind and Papi had given his word — the collection was his.

This was to be a family decision and demanded family action. Then. Not tomorrow or the next day. Tios and tias, primos and primas, and los abuelos were summoned. Just in case: bring wrapping paper and newspaper to wrap with; Scotch tape — we're sure to run out; ribbons; writing paper and pens for notes. We'll have a lot to wrap and it has to be done before Connor starts exams on Tuesday. "Oh, and Miguelito. You're not going to school tomorrow. We've got to take care of this."

Cuban coffee — enough to jump start several small countries in Europe — was brewed; Abuela started pulling out coffee cans of flan. Yup, she did it the old-fashioned way. This factory was going to operate on a sugar high and a caffeine rush.

When, within half an hour, the clan was gathered, Mikey stated his case.

Everyone knew and loved Connor, he was familia now. And last night, after everyone had left, Connor talked about the pain of his Marine friends... that so many of them had forgotten what it is to be a kid... they've seen so much war and live with such fear... How Abuelo always taught all of them that Christmas was for the child, the kid in each of us and these guys had lost their Kid-Inside. That the Collection was Mikey's and Papi had told him that he could do whatever he wanted with it. You can't give a Marine a Teddy Bear — what would people think if they saw a Marine with his own Teddy Bear? But we can give them trucks and make them personal from la familia.

"God, can that kid talk," thought Abuelo, who stood, even before Mikey had finished. Case closed. *"Vengan. Come."* And with one word he was headed to the garage, bringing out and opening the ladder and climbing to the attic to pull down forty-nine years of pristinely kept boxes of Hess trucks — unopened, of almost inestimable value — a perfect collection destined for as many Marines.

The dining room table and floors became a multilingual wrapping factory: *"Da me el Scotch tape," "Mire, corta lo* here," "Do you want *un cafecito.*"

In the end, there remained one truck. Smaller than any other. The oldest. The first he had bought for his future family. Abuelo held it gently, calmly, proudly, and with a determination that silenced the entire assembly. He grabbed Miguelito and *le dio un abrazo tan fuerte* – gave him a hug so tight – it sent warm shivers through every family member. "Miguelito, you wrap this one for Tio Connor."

"*Hijo, ven,*" Abuelo directed Papi. And, moving to the kitchen, he grabbed paper and a pen and directed Papi, "My English is not so good. Write…."

> Estimado Connor.
>
> Please pardon me. I do not speak or write English well.
>
> Through Miguelito we have learned how much so many of you Marines don't like or want to be thanked "for your service." We have begun to understand that we can never understand what your service has meant to you and those you love.
>
> We've also learned how many of you live with pain and fear and even sleep with your guns close at hand. That many of you have lost the all-important child-inside.
>
> Truly you are family now. And there are some things you should know about our family - your

family. We believe that kids should always be kids - deep in their hearts and for as long as they live.

We have taught our children and grandchildren that the greatest way to love another person is to pray for him.

Even though we believe that everyone should have at least one Teddy Bear in their life and a toy at Christmas, Miguellito has insisted that we cannot give a Marine a Teddy Bear.

So, Abuela and I hope you will please accept this simple gift — bought in my first weeks in the United States, even before I knew Abuela.

It is not a Teddy Bear but it is a toy and, we hope more than a toy. Please put it next to your bed or where you will see it every night as you turn out the light. Please let it be a constant reminder that we do and will forever pray for you. You are family and because you are loved you are prayed for and because you are prayed for you are loved.

If the time ever comes when your Kid-Inside is strong and happy and free and you do not need this gift, please give it to another Marine or someone who is in pain and explain that he, too, is prayed for and loved. And, if he ever wants or needs a great Cuban meal, he only needs to knock on the door and show his truck.

With a strong hug from all of your family, we wish you a most Merry Christmas.

Abuelo

Wherever there was room enough to sit and write, family members began their own versions of Abuelo's letter and carefully taped them to forty-eight other boxes.

"Pues," ordered Papi. "Call Tios Nick and Connor and tell them we are coming."

"Papi! It's Sunday night! They have their meeting."

"Pues! No importa! We are going! Now!"

And so it happened that Miguelito's and Tios Nick's and Connor's entire family arrived at the Sigma Chi House — Wise Men bearing not Toys-For-Tots but Trucks-For-Marines. The rest is unimportant. Tio Connor — Secretary of Defense and Secretary of the Navy — would ensure that every gift was carefully guarded and personally and proudly delivered.

And we pray that the Kid-Inside will sleep tonight without fear, without pain and with a smile on his face.

"A Boy Wins" Kinda Christmas

*I*n *opening, let me introduce two characters who give life to today's Christmas Gift:*

Nearly four decades ago, at the beginning of his hometown First Mass, a young priest introduced one of the concelebrants as "Old Weird Frank." Moments later, a stately matron objected "How can you call that priest 'Weird'?" But, how else can you described a grown adult who talks to the statues in his Christmas Crib?

Tom Ross is one of my favorite Sigma Chis and heroes. A Cleveland cop, he spent years locking up and putting away child abusers. Earlier this year, this Marine by history and disposition and his wife learned that their son, Andrew Jonathan, has autism. At the time of the initial diagnosis, a fellow parent told Tom, "We may never win this war; we may never win many battles. But when we do, they will be enormous, so celebrate them."

◄○►◄○►◄○►◄○►◄○►◄○►◄○►◄○►◄○►◄○►◄○►

There's a part of me that wants to call them the Three Wise Men of Western Little Havana. But that would almost be too easy; it would certainly be trite, and I don't do trite. Besides, they weren't always three and unless we call them the Two Little Wise Men and the Old Dude Wise Man, well….

Puros Gringos (absolute Gringos) from Cleveland, Tom and Melanie found the perfect fixer-up for their would-be growing family. On the western fringes of Little Havana and a block away from the church and school they planned would be the second home for their future kids. It captured Melanie's heart when she realized that — through the magic of perfectly placed windows, mirrors and picture frame glass and with a stealth that would make the collective mouths of the CIA drool — she could survey every square inch of home and yard with just a turn of the head. Tom fixer-upper-ed, Melanie planned and decorated. Together they learned the differences among *café con leche, un cortadito* (a huge serving of Cuban coffee), and u*n cafecito* (a small Cuban coffee); *mariquitos* (banana chips), *tostones* (fried banana patties) and *platanos maduros* (fried bananas). And, despite their so obvious gringohood, in their neighbors they found three generations of adopted *abuelos, hermanos, and hijos* — grandparents, brothers and sisters, and kids — they never knew were part of their Ancestry.com profiles. Abuelo shared mangoes and limones; Abuela taught Melanie how to choose the perfect rice-maker; Mami and Papi became their Miami-versions of brother and sister, introducing them to Dolphins and Hurricanes football, and knowing the best mechanics, physicians, and pastelerias (pastry shops) — all either cousins- or brothers-owned or owned by *un buen amigo* — a good friend.

Miguelito? He simply adopted them as another extension of his almost infinite circle of aunts and uncles — Tio Tom and Tia Mel — who, he assumed, like so many of his other tios and tias would one day gift him with another *"hermanito"* — little brother.

When that time did arrive, Mikey immediately assumed his role as Guardian Protector. In fact, he became so protective that he could spend hours just watching AJ sleep or crawl or begin to walk. He talked to him unceasingly — about his own home, about school, and swimming and sports, all his tios and tias, his adventures riding his bike and the places they would one day explore together. About being an altar server for *el Padre Pancho el Estrano* – Weird Father Frank.

And, the truth is that Father Frank was strange – weird. So *flaco* – thin – he was once described as being able to hide behind a pencil. Now almost completely bald, for decades almost half-a-century ago he wore his sortta reddish, thinning hair in a 'fro and sported a small gold cross in his ear before pierced ears on men was a fashion statement. It was not so strange that he collect-ed Christmas cribs from around the world; but it was weird that he talked to the figures in his manger scenes. And, when I say he "talked" to the figures, I mean he talked to the figures. Not just "Good morning, Mommy Mary" or "Good night, Daddy Joseph." But real conver-sations with all of the personalities – the shepherd boys and girls, the Wise Men and the Angels and the Holy Family. Depending on his mood and the issue at hand, sometimes, short snippets of conversation. Sometimes in-depth explorations of theological issues from his and their points of view.

Father Frank had *nacimientos* – Christmas creches – in school show cases and church offices, and on dis-play year-round on nearly a dozen shelves in the church sacristy. From Korea and Japan, Tanzania and Russia, and just about every country taught about in geography classes. In glass and ceramic, wood and straw, and clay.

He greeted and conversed with them all day, every day — by himself and when others were present.

And, just as Frank talked to the people of his crèches, Mikey talked to AJ. Visits were such a part of life in Mikeylandia that, three-plus years after he met the newborn, the visits and monologues didn't change. It was as if Mikey lived to make AJ smile and laugh — jumping with all his clothes on into AJ's plastic pool, making balloon animals and painting both their faces on football game days.

By age three, AJ knew Mikey's schedules. He would watch him from the window as he trekked to school and wait for him at the door when he returned. At his own home or at Mikey's, AJ would stare in silent wonder as Miquelito did homework and neither family ever knew quite for sure in which home the two Wise Boys would have dinner. So, there were always leftovers for the not infrequent unexpected quests in their homes. And, at Sunday Masses, AJ would sit facing the front door waiting for Mikey and the processional cross to lead lectors, candle bearers, and Father Frank to the altar. His gaze never lost sight of his Cubanito brother. In fact, as the entrance procession passed by, it was not unknown for AJ to slide from of Tom's or Mel's guarding grip into the aisle and, with one hand, grab Mikey's robe and boldly accompany him into the sanctuary. All with Father Frank's obvious approval and to the congregation's gentle smiles. But, through it all — at play, at home, in church, everywhere, AJ maintained the silence of the young autistic — never uttering a word.

It was once rumored that Father Frank was so old that St. Peter himself presided at his ordination. At an age way-past retirement, the former missioner to Japan accepted the one-priest parish's plea for a helping padre to handle English language services. His Spanglish was essentially limited to ordering coffee in cafeterias and *Buenos Dias* and *Hola*, but to the *viejos* (old folks) and *ninos* (kids), to the adolescents and the *novios* (engaged), in fact, throughout Western Little Havana, he was known as *el cura Felix Navidad* — the priest who wished everyone Merry Christmas all the time, all year long — and *el cura estrano* — the weird priest — who talked to the shepherds and Jesus and Joseph and Mary of Christmas cribs everywhere.

One day, after overhearing others speaking about the weird priest who talks to statues, Mikey decided to solve the mysteries of WHY? and ask just that: "Padre, why do you say 'Good morning, Mother Mary' and 'Good morning, Father Joseph' and talk to the statues all the time? Why do you always tell people 'Merry Christmas' even in the summer?"

"Wow!" the priest responded. "I guess because they teach me the lessons of love and life and I don't want to forget them.

"Mommy Mary teaches us about the love of God as accepting, as hoping, as promising and nurturing. Papi Joseph reminds me that God is protecting and gentle, strong and patient and, somehow, always here for us and with us.

"I talk to the people of the Christmas cribs because whether things are going well or are really difficult, at one time or another they've all been through what I am going through. The shepherds knew fear and loneliness, poverty and struggles, hope and promise, pain and mercy and comfort; they had dreams for their children and thoughts of the future. The Wise Men had learned long ago that all their riches could not satisfy the longings of their hearts or bring them true happiness. They wandered far from home and comfort and all that they knew searching for the gifts – not that they brought – but that only God can give.

"And the angels remind me that as a missioner, as a person of faith, as child of God, in my life and with my words I must declare 'Glory to God in the Highest and Peace to his People on Earth.'

"'I love you' and 'mother' and 'father' are the most sacred words we can say because they tell us something about God. And, I say 'Merry Christmas' because one of the names we have for God is 'The Word' and when I use these words and I talk to my friends the statues, I am reminded of God and that He is everywhere."

So it happened that as Christmas Eve approached, Abuelo and Abuela, Mami and Papi, all the tios and tias, "the whole *fam-damnily*" as Papi would say, imitating American slang, issued not an invitation but a directive to Tom and Melanie, daughter Caroline and AJ: they would be part of *Noche Buena al estilo Cubano* — Christmas Eve Miami Cuban style. Of course, the invitation also came with a warning: Cuban-American Christmas Eves are all-day affairs beginning eight to twelve hours before dinner when the men prepare the *Caja China* — the Cuban-style barbeque grill for roasting a whole pig — and only end with the family caravan to evening Mass. Santa will come only after Mass and when kids are tugged snuggly away.

And so, on Christmas Eve, Tom and Mel joined la familia for dinner and the trek to church. Mikey took his leave long before the extended family and staked out prize seating. He was vested in his long white choir robe and Christmas-holiday-red cincture and with processional cross in hand when the fam-damnily arrived. But rather than join Tom and Mel and Caroline as they walked up the aisle, AJ grabbed Miquelio's robe and refused to let go. The child who did not speak did not speak. But, the look on his face said it all: "I'm with Mikey. I'm with Mikey. I'm with Mikey."

Tom's Marine training kicked into play. He knew instinctively that a three-year old determined to stay glued to his adopted uncle was a force no Jarhead could counter. "Besides," he thought, "with Mikey and a whole church looking out for him, how much trouble can he get into?" For his part, Father Frank temporarily ceded leadership to a ten-year-old altar boy and his trusted sidekick, and from the church door, began to intone The Christmas Proclamation. Having declared "The Nativity of Our Lord according to the Flesh," Father Frank began a monologue-dialogue with the statue of the Christ Child in his arms. "Yes! I think so. A good idea. Yes! Christmas is for children. Sure!"

And, because he lived the Missioner's Spirit that says rules and norms, including rules and norms about celebrating Mass, are really only guidelines, even – or especially – at Christmas Eve Mass, Frank bent low to Mikey's never-speaking sidekick and whispered, "AJ, could you, please, carry my little friend here for me. I'm kindda old and he's a little heavy."

Now, it is said of the Proclaiming Angels that "the Glory of the Lord shone round about them" and a Fourth Century theologian has taught us "The Glory of God is the human person fully alive." In that moment, as he cradled his Sacred Charge to the altar manager, the Glory of the Lord shined bright from AJ's face and he was fully alive – the Glory of God.

As the procession moved toward the altar, at the family pew, Mikey the Cross-Bearer and the Christ-bearing AJ paused. Paused while Mikey smiled a Miguelito smile. Paused and AJ spoke. "Mommy! Mommy! Daddy! Daddy!"

And Father Frank understood "the Word has been made Flesh and dwells amongst us" and God's greatest gifts are the world's smallest – a smile, a word, a name; the gentleness of kindness, mercy and compassion; the strength of a constant and non-judging companion; the goodness of one who knows us – sometimes better than we know ourselves – and loves us simply because we are.

To quote my friend and hero Tom Ross, "In the on-going and brutal struggle of Autism vs. Boy, today BOY wins!"

<hr />

In September 2019, after moving to the Major Seminary Building at Maryknoll, Father Frank sent an update: "I now converse with my crucifixes and crosses… I decorated the walls of my new room (cell?) with paintings, icons, prints and enough crosses that I created what I call my 'cross section' which is at least ten feet of wall space occupied with the dying Jesus. This cross-section is right above the head of my bed so I can converse and dream and love Him at His crucifixion. I talk with alive people now and then also."

Oooye Gooooey Mangos and St. Francis

Born on the Fourth of August — some might say a month too late for someone who could appropriately be described as a living fireworks show — with brownish-blonde hair and blue eyes inherited from his grandmother, Mikey was as All-Miami as *picadillo* and pizza, *frijoles negros* and hot dogs, Cuban coffee and The Hurricanes and The Dolphins. But as we've learned through the years, he's always been a puzzlement.

Now to understand this story, you must first understand the neighborhood. Some laughingly say it should be called "Shhhh! Don't tell," because sixty-plus years ago, when today's *abuelos* and *abuelas* — grandparents — first moved in, that's the way it grew: without the required permits and pretty much "Shhhh! Don't tell." A garage converted to a bedroom here. An extra bedroom and bath added there. Sometimes even a whole second-floor suite. With the work completed almost always by *un amigo de mi primo* — "a friend of my cousin." In a decade or so, those post-World War II "all-look-just-the-same" little houses were home to expanding families of new and not-so-new refuges, opening small shops and workshops, restaurants and groceries.

Now, more than six decades later, Mikey's *abuelos* had never moved. This was more than home. It was where they had planted roots, reared their family and grown old together. This was also where, except for his family, Abuelo's two greatest prides were the giant mango trees in the back yard, dominating the entire neighborhood. And, Abuelo confidently declared, his were the best mangos in the world.

Because they shared the same values, it was where, having met in the Maryknoll Volunteer Corps in Tanzania — (Can you imagine two Cuban-American Miami Hurricane alumni teachers first meeting in East Africa?) — Mikey's parents decided to rear their family.

Roots and family, traditions and values are important. For a while not much changed in "Shhhh! Don't tell." On occasion a family might move to Kendal or abuelos might retire to be with their kids in Vero Beach or even South Carolina. Then, just about a decade ago, two months into hurricane season and just at the beginning of mango season, the neighborhood changed! Actually, depending on how you counted, it changed once, or twice or five times. Oh, how it changed!

At almost one and the same instant, Mikey was brought home from the hospital – for the first time – all blonde fuzz and blue eyes. And, *las mujeres Americanas* – the American women, all four of them, moved into the "Shhhh Don't Tell" house next to his abuelos.

For a few days, the whispers and comments clashed with each other. "*Ah, que guapo, que lindo, un rubio! Fijese!* How handsome, how beautiful! A blonde! Imagine that." And "*Quatro mujeres. Viejas! Son Americanas! Quines son?*" "Four women! They're old. They're Americans! Who are they?"

Mikey?

Well, you know Mikey (and we'll get back to him in about a literary decade). But, the women? After a few days of what seemed like seclusion and secrecy, they wandered the neighborhood, door-to-door, introducing themselves. Trying to explain the somewhat unexplainable. They were, they said through Sister Grace, the only ones who spoke Spanish, semi-retired Catholic mission-ary Sisters – from the Philippines, Japan, the Sudan, and Guatemala. New York winters had proven just too cold and they came to "Shhhh! Don't Tell" to open a little house of prayer. Not quite a cloister, they explained, but a place from which they could help others by being a constant prayerful support. "We place the hurting and their pains in the loving heart of God and we accompa-ny them on their journeys," she explained. "Oh, and we make bread for the poor and for our friends."

They were, Sister Grace continued, committed to changing the world quietly. Being strength to the weak and broken and hope to the hopeless through prayer. Their *Casa San Francisco de Asis* was dedicated to pray-ing throughout the day the Saint's "The Praises of God":

You are holy, Lord, the only God, and Your
deeds are wonderful.
You are strong, great, the Most High.
You are Almighty.

You are Good, all Good, supreme Good,
Lord God, living and true.
You are love and wisdom, humility and
endurance.
You are rest and peace, joy and gladness.

You are justice, beauty. Gentleness.
Our protector, guardian and defender.
Our courage, our haven and our hope.

You are our faith, our great consolation,
our eternal life.
Great and Wonderful Lord, God Almighty,
Merciful Savior.

Over the years, and depending on the wind and
weather, from mid-afternoon to evening, the neighborhood would fill with the ohh-so-subtle aroma of
fresh-baking bread, and, if you listened carefully, you
could hear the chant four times a day – "You are holy
Lord, the only God..." It was a sound as familiar to
Miguelito as his parents' laughter or Abuela's nightly
benediction *"Que duermas con los angelitos"* – "May you
sleep with the angels." Mikey grew up with the words.
They may, in fact, have been the first English he learned
as they wafted from the tiny chapel next door or filled
the evening from the garden under the overhanging
branches of Abuelo's mango trees.

As he grew from diapers to toddler, from walking
to running – non-stop and everywhere, from tricycle
to training wheels and bike, Miguelito also grew from
play-on-the-floor little toy wagon to full-scale big boy's
wagons made for hauling all sorts of things. And, year-
after-year, mango season after mango season, Abuelo
taught Mikey two great lessons: Mangos are God's favorite fruit and his most delicious, oooey, gooey gift to
His People, and mangos are a gift to be shared. It seemed

to Mikey this was Abuelo's most-favorite-thing-in-the-world to do — give away his mangos.

Abuela, Mikey's grandmother, insisted that a first stop of the Mango Man and his red wagon was to be the house next door, for the gentle women who prayed and made bread for their neighbors and the poor. And, one day, Sister Grace added a request to her gentle "Thank You:

"Why don't you bring us the really bruised mangos, the ones your grandfather doesn't give away."

"But, but… they're ooooey, messy," Miguel protested.

"Yes," replied Sister Grace. "There's an oooey, gooey part of all of us, but God can make even that something special."

"Do you know," she inquired, "Why we make bread for the poor?"

And slowly, quietly out poured the story of their home's namesake and how in the year 1219, during the Fifth Crusade, St. Francis and Brother Illuminato travelled — mostly by foot — from Italy to Damietta on the northern coast of Egypt because Francis wanted to plead with Christian Crusaders and Malik al-Kamil, the Sultan of Egypt, for an end to the war and to save thousands and thousands of Christian and Muslim lives. Francis and Illuminato dared to walk across the no-man's-land between the two armies and Francis and the Sultan spent days respecting each other, listening to each other, sharing with each other, maybe even praying at the same times and letting God be God.

In the end, explained Sister Grace, Francis left Damietta, believing he had failed because he could not convince the warring sides to accept peace. But, "and here's Francis's kind of little miracle," whispered Sister Grace. Almost two years later, the Sultan had an opportunity to destroy all the European Christians because the Nile had flooded their camps, leaving them trapped by mud and dying of diseases.

"Instead," Sister Grace continued, "every day he sent them 50,000 loaves of bread and 1,000 bushels of barley for their animals and saved the lives of his sworn enemies.

"And so, in honor of St. Francis and the Sultan, we make bread and, when we can, we share it with those whom others do not see or do not think about or do not like. And now, if you will share your grandfather's ugliest, ooooey, gooeyist mangos, maybe we can do something special with them."

◄o►◄o►◄o►◄o►◄o►◄o►◄o►◄o►◄o►◄o►◄o►

Mango season is over.

Tonight is *Noche Buena*, "the Good Night," Christmas Eve. Throughout "Shhh! Don't Tell" abuelos and hijos —

grandfathers and sons — have spent hours preparing the *lechon* — roast pork. Abuelas and hijas huddle over their *frijoles negros y arroz* — black beans and rice. And, as the sun sets, if you are just quiet enough, you might hear:

> You are holy, Lord, the only God, and
> Your deeds are wonderful.
> You are strong, great, the Most High.
> You are Almighty.

And some time tomorrow morning, Miguelito's and other families throughout "Shhh! Don't Tell" will discover on their doorsteps small bundles of homemade bread and jars of mango marmalade, with the handwritten note:

> You are Good, all Good, supreme
> Good, Lord God, living and true.
> You are love and wisdom, humility
> and endurance.
> You are rest and peace, joy
> and gladness.

> You are justice, beauty. Gentleness.
> Our protector, guardian and defender.
> Our courage, our haven and our hope.

You are our faith, our great consolation,
our eternal life.
Great and Wonderful Lord, God
Almighty, Merciful Savior.

1995

Saint Stanislaus Day

Mikey was ready. He had never been so ready in his whole life.

He was Rudolf the Red-Nosed Reindeer, the Three Wise Men, the Archangel Gabriel, all of the Shepherds, and Greg LeMond, his favorite Tour de France champion bike racer, all rolled into one and now he was ready. He stood, his bicycle between his legs, peering as far down the street as he could see. His eyes fixed on the corner where he knew the car would turn and, when it did, he would spring into action. He would go racing down the street to announce to everyone who would hear, to everyone who could hear, "Merry Christmas." He would announce it quietly, in a whisper. And they would never hear, but Mikey would know and just knowing was all that was important. It was a secret, the first ever "secret Christmas."

Mikey kept it secret. Well, almost. He only told one person and Mikey knew that Father Mark would never tell.

Way up the street the light changed – shining red in Miguelito's direction. That meant it was green now in the direction from which Mikey was expecting to see Tio Rickey's car. Mikey loved the word – *Tio* – Uncle. In fact, he had decided that, next to *Mami* and *Papi*, Tios were just about the greatest thing in all the world. Tio Ricky wasn't really Tio Ricky. Mikey's real tios were still in Cuba – far, far away. Mikey did not understand much about Cuba, only that things were very, very bad there and his parents had – much like the family of the Nino Jesus – left home and came to a place that was safe, where Mikey could grow up and go to school and his parents would not have to worry so much about him. But, leaving Cuba had meant that Mikey had no tios, no tias.

That is, until Tio Ricky. He had volunteered to coach Mikey's Koury League baseball team, and after a while, he appointed himself Miguelito's "adopted uncle." They did everything together – Miami Hurricanes' baseball and football games (the football team wasn't the greatest this year, but the baseball team went to the College World Series, again). Tio Ricky knew everything about baseball. He was great.

They would go to the beach, always with Ricky's girlfriend; but that was alright. He made sure that Miguelito did his homework. He went to Parent-Teacher night at school. Miquelito was there when Ricky bought his new car and celebrated with him when he got his first real job. They were a family. Ricky had become part of his and he was part of Ricky's.

And today was the most important family day ever. Ricky's younger brother, Joey, was coming home. It was Noche Buena and Christmas and the Fourth of July and Jose's birthday all rolled into one. And it was a surprise — surprise because Ricky's and Joey's mother, the Senora Gutierrez, did not know. Al least, she did not know it was today.

She thought it was going to be next week. But it wasn't; it was today, the Eleventh of April — a Surprise Christmas.

Mrs. Gutierrez had carefully kept the map tracing Joey's travels. From his military base in Georgia, to France, to Germany, to Hungary, and finally to Bosnia as a "peace keeper." From Ricky, Miguelito learned the whole history. He knew all about Serbs and Croats and Muslims, the Bosnians and the U.N. Mikey listened carefully and he learned, especially because, when speaking to Miguelito, Ricky always referred to "your Tio Jose" and would reassure the boy "I've told him all about you. We're going to have some great times when he gets back."

Now he was back. Tio's car had made the turn and was coming down the street and only Mikey knew the secret. Mrs. Gutierrez didn't know. That's what would make it a surprise. Only Mikey and his tios, and in a minute, Father Mark.

Father Mark was great. Mikey had already told him part of what was happening and had explained to him how important it was. About the map, and Tio's travel, and homecoming, and how Mrs. Gutierrez stopped every night on her way home from work to attend the six o'clock Mass and pray for Jose "and all of our boys and girls over there." That she had refused to take down the Christmas tree. The presents were still under the tree and she said that she would have *Noche Buena* – Christmas Eve – only when the whole family, including Mikey, could be together.

So, they had planned it all – Mikey, Father Mark, and Tio. And now the plan was in action. Mikey pedaled faster than he had ever pedaled before. Blazing down the street, even as Tio's car drew ever closer. Through the parking lot, up the sidewalk, between buildings, around a corner. At the sacristy door he jumped off and pulled his bike inside, and almost completely out of breath, shouted a whisper, "They're here. He's home. Please, Father. You promised! Please." It was a statement, an argument, a declaration. Almost a direct order, issued as the boy pulled on his cassock and doffed his surplice. "Please."

"Besides. Jesus would do it," he added, sealing his position with a smile.

What could the priest do? The pastor would be furious — maybe. But a promise was a promise. Although he did not quite remember ever having made a promise, Mikey had sort of just started planning it and Father Mark got trapped. Under his breath, mostly to himself, the priest mumbled his assent, "St. Stanislaus, bishop and martyr (whose feast day it was) will just have to wait. God, I hope there aren't any Poles out there today. And please, don't anybody tell the pope — Stanislaus is his favorite. Then I'll really be in trouble."

"Christmas it is, Miguel. But, if we're going to do Christmas, let's do it right. Light some charcoal and get the incense ready. I'll incense the book at the Gospel time, and after the boys have presented the gifts, I'll incense them, too. Just like in Sunday Mass."

The other altar boy just stood there. Confused. He had no idea what was happening. "Bring in the big book off the reading stand," Father Mark directed him. And, when it was delivered and pages turned, the priest told him, "Now, take it back."

"Okay, boys. We'll come in from the back – like Sunday. That way I'll get to talk to Ricky for a minute. Make sure she's already here."

"Yes, Father. I saw her when I was lighting the candles."

"Okay. Good. Let's go."

In the parking lot, Miguelito ran to hug his Tio Ricky and was lifted off the ground by Jose, whose hug was strong and tight and all the way to the heart.

"Alright, guys," the priest directed. "Wait until I'm all the way to the altar. Then you come in and sit in the back. Miguel will bring the cross down at the Offertory and you follow him up with the gifts. After that, you can go back and sit with your mother — if she's able to sit at that point."

At the door of the church, Father began in a booming voice: "The twenty-fifth day of December: In the five-thousand, one hundred and ninety-ninth year of the creation of the world..." Heads turned, pages rustled. People were mystified as he continued The Christmas Proclamation. When they reached the altar and Father Mark began the opening prayer — "Father, You make this holy night radiant with the splendor of Jesus Christ, our light" — Miguel could hardly keep from laughing.

Months earlier, he had declared his intention to become a priest "because you don't have to get married and you can stand at the door and shake hands with all the people." Now he added another reason to his list — because you can watch the faces of the people when you do something they don't expect or you say something they don't like. Like the time Father talked about cheating and used the example of a grocer who sneaks some rotten yucca into the bag along with the good ones and the man who owns the market on the corner could hardly sit still; or the time he said that parents must set a good example for their children and not abuse alcohol and the neighborhood drunk, who everyone knows goes to Mass on Sunday after being drunk all Friday night and Saturday and beating his kids, couldn't stop squirming. Mikey loved to sit up on the altar platform and watch. He thought it another good reason for being a priest. And now he could watch the chaos of people turning pages and looking at each other all bewildered.

Finally, Father Mark stopped and told the congregation, "Put your missalettes away. I've decided to say the Midnight Mass of Christmas today. And that's what I'm going to do. Just because I decided. Gee whiz, we don't really know when Jesus was born. Who really cares? And, if you do, well maybe you shouldn't. It's April 11, the Feast of St. Stanislas. So what!?! Christmas is supposed to be all year long. At least that's what we keep saying in December. So. Peace be with you..."

"And also with you," the congregation responded. Although, in truth, a few people did get up and head for the door.

Father finished the readings — all from the Midnight Mass of Christmas. But now he realized what Miguel had already seen — the people were thoroughly confused. It was alright.

"Serendipity," he said, beginning his homily. "Serendipity. 'An unexpected, pleasant event.' That's the dictionary definition. Serendipity should be part of the spiritual life of each of us. It's the realization that God has become Man and dwells among us. Serendipity is the realization that God loves us so much that He makes our lives holy by the mystery of His unique sharing in them.

"When we forget that, when we restrict and limit Christmas to just one day of the year, when we are willing to give gifts to others but are less willing to give to ourselves, when we are less willing to give ourselves, when we spend in the expectation of receiving but are not willing to expend ourselves because that's what Jesus did... Then we miss serendipity and we miss Christmas... I meant what I said at the beginning of Mass. Christmas is supposed to be all year round. So, Merry Christmas."

Clearly now, some of those still in the church were convinced the priest was crazy.

"If you only knew," Miguel thought, as the Prayers of the Faithful were said. "It is Christmas... A great, secret Christmas."

He waived off the other altar boy, indicating that he would carry the cross to lead up the gifts. As he approached the processional cross, he reached down, pulled up the hem of his cassock, dug into the back pocket of his jeans, and produced a bright red Christmas cap that he tugged down on his head.

This was almost too much for many of those who had already begun to believe that the priest was "a little crazy." Now, they thought, his craziness was infectious and Miguel was the first victim of the epidemic.

Tios Jose and Ricky were waiting at the back of the church when Miguel approached with the cross. He spun around smartly and started toward the altar. Mrs. Gutierrez didn't even look up as he passed. And, she didn't see her sons until after Father Mark had accepted the gifts of bread and water and wine, thanked the boys, and in a very loud voice declared, "Merry Christmas, Senora Gutierrez."

She looked up. She shouted. The boys didn't walk; they ran to her. There were *abrazos* – hugs – all round. Quietly, tentatively, from up on the altar, Miguelito started to clap. Then Father Mark, then someone else, and slowly, slowly Christmas came in waves of applause – on April 11 – the Feast of St. Stanislaus, bishop and martyr.

Why not? Christmas should be every day of the year.

Mikey Knows

To his father he had always been Miguel.

To his *madre* — Miguelito.

For me. Well. I have just always thought of him as "Mikey."

To some — those who only knew him as the bus driver's son, attending the parochial grade school in South Miami serviced by his mother's small, struggling bus service — he was the cow-eyed little boy who hardly ever spoke. On the morning and afternoon routes through Miami suburbs he almost hid behind his mother's seat, listening intently to sixth, seventh and eighth-graders chatting in Spanish and English of their spending sprees at the local malls and the cars they would get when they turned sixteen.

In the classroom, he was even more silent. Raising his hand only, it seemed, when he was absolutely confident that he knew the correct answer. And always with a "Yes, Ma'am" or "No, Ma'am."

To the merchants along Miami's *Calle Ocho* — the heart of Little Havana — the little mom-and-pop stores with the bananas and mangos, the avocados and sugar cane open for grabs in the outside stalls — he was a puzzling terror on wheels — the two wheels of the bike his father bought over a year ago and repaired, spruced up and painted as a gift for *El Dia de los Tres Reyes Magos* — the Feast of the Three Kings, when, by tradition, Cuban children receive their special "Christmas gifts" from the Three Wise Men.

They all knew Mikey — doing wheelies on the sidewalks, showing off with balancing acts that defied gravity, scooting between and forcing cars to screeching halts. Many suspected him — even accused him, though never to either his face or that of his parents — of minor, borderline misdemeanors and mischief. But it was only suspicion.

Mikey was a puzzlement — hell on wheels. A terror. A holy terror. A holy, hell-on-wheels terror of a puzzlement. And when that special Monday came — the Mon-

day of the week before Christmas — Mikey was set free.
Free from school and teachers. Free from *Mami,* who did
not drive her school bus during summers, and therefore,
kept him under careful watch but would now work as
a gift wrapper at Burdines in order to make Christmas
money.

Free from the ever-present gaze of Papi that roped
him into the neighborhood during school time week-
ends.

Now, the week before Christmas, Mikey was free. It
was just the two of them — Mikey and his bike and a big,
wide, wonderful world to know and to explore. There
was only one rule, never spoken. Not even understood
by his parents. A rule that Mikey had established for
himself in order to avoid Papi's anger and a consequent
punishment: "Be home when his parents arrive at the
end of the day."

For a kid of eleven — for a holy terror, hell-on-wheels,
puzzlement of a kid — Mikey was especially careful in
his observance of this rule.

And so it came to pass that during this Christmas
holiday, Mikey was, for the first time ever, free and on
his own, with just his bike and wanderlust.

Mikey was exhilarated, thrilled by the freedom of
the holiday. He and his Three Wise Men bike were everywhere. One morning, even before his mother's car
had disappeared down the street, he was off — destina-

tion unknown, ultimately crossing the huge Bay Bridge to Key Biscayne, carrying his bike down to the water's edge, enjoying a long, cool swim, drying off in the warmth of the December sun. Then settling himself on the beach to ponder, as only an eleven-year-old can, the wonder and majesty of Creation.

Mikey was no scholar, and certainly no theologian. But he had learned from his mother and grown to appreciate through his father's silent assents to her declarations of faith, that all this — the deep oceans, the colors of the tropical fish that had been nibbling at his toes, the warmth of the sun — they were all reflections of God's loving goodness to His people. And so Miguelito enjoyed them, and after a child's fashion, he gave thanks.

On another occasion, having prepared for himself a backpack filled with sodas, some left over guava pastries and croquetas from the night before, Mikey and his bike wandered among the domino players in the small parks along the Miami River and explored the docks and piers of the Miami water front.

At one point, he happened upon an old woman, somewhat bent over and truly dirty, pushing, to Mikey's absolute amazement, a grocery cart filled with all kinds of the most unbelievable goods. There were aluminum cans and old dresses, pots and pans that looked as though they had never been washed, and every kind of old clothing imaginable. It was a wonder to Mikey. He had sometimes seen such women from the window of his mother's school bus or passing through some of the back streets of Little Havana. But now, for the first time, there was an opportunity to see one up close. To stop, get off his bike, and actually talk with her.

And so, in the shade of an old poinciana tree just outside Jose Marti Park, Miguel stopped and they began to talk. About her cart and where she had been. How she lived under a bridge that crossed the river. Jobs she had had, his family. They shared lunch together — she had never had croquetas but she liked them and reckoned that Mikey was right when he said they tasted even better warm and fresh from the oven.

In the background, Cuban and Puerto Rican *villancicos* — Christmas carols — blared from a stereo shop's outside speakers and she asked what the words meant. After all, "What does a broken down old Irish Catholic crazy lady from Boston" know about "all those Spanish words," she said with a laughing smile.

Miguel translated. It was, indeed, a strange combination — the Irish bag lady from Boston and a Cuban-American holy terror on wheels translating for her the rhythmic invitations to "come to the stable and see the Baby."

As the afternoon shadows deepened, she announced that it was time for her to "be moving on." But she paused for a moment as Mikey mounted his bike to say,

"Thanks, Mickey. You don't mind of I call you Mickey, but it makes you just a little bit Boston Irish if I do, and I'm just a little homesick right now. Thanks, Mickey, for the pleasure of your company and all those cockets, croquets...."

"Croquetas," he said. "Merry Christmas, señora. Feliz Navidad."

"Sure, and Merry Christmas to you, Mickey," she laughed.

Miguelito's mind flew almost as fast as his feet peddled. Remember the Rule: Be home before Mami and Papi. But he also remembered the richest girl in the classroom, who just last week when Sister Irene asked what they would show to the Christ Child and where they would take him, had shouted "Bloomingdales" and then laughed at Mikey when he asked, "What's that?"

"Why," thought Mikey, "the old lady is like Joseph and Mary. She doesn't even have a place to live tonight."

For Mikey, it seemed as though the world just continued to grow wider and wider over the next few days, expanding with each turn of his bike's wheels. Including more and more people. There were some Black Haitian kids who spoke a very strange kind of Spanish — it had to be Spanish, Mikey had reasoned, because in Miami, if it wasn't English, it had to be Spanish. But he didn't understand their Spanish no matter how hard he tried. He did know that they played basketball, though, just like he did; so it didn't matter how well or poorly they communicated; they were kids just like he was.

One afternoon, having left home this time with nothing to drink, he followed a stream of men and women into a big old store front/warehouse-like building where people were passing out meals. Mikey really wasn't interested in the food; all he wanted was some cold water. But, after getting a drink from the water fountain, he spent time playing "paddy cake" and "How big is the baby? So Big!" with a smiling, cooing infant whose mother was explaining to someone how they were — all three, mother, father and baby — living in an old car parked up the street.

Mikey listened intently, all the while still playing "How big is the baby?" and "peak-a-boo." And, when the couple left, he followed them, quietly and somewhat at a distance. As they climbed into their old car, parked not too far away, he approached. "Here, sir," he offered, opening his backpack and pouring out onto the car hood a seemingly endless mound of sandwiches and *galletas Cubanas* — Cuban crackers.

Before anyone could say anything, Mikey was off again searching for new worlds to explore.

The week sped by much like that. There were little things and some not so little. Like the Thursday afternoon when, just a block away from home a car cut him off and he fell, suffering a huge gash in his arm. Mikey tried to brave it out and hide both the pain and the blood, but a neighbor saw and his mother could hardly miss the expressions on his face. Mikey ended up in Jackson Memorial Hospital's emergency room. It was a long wait until some really nice doctor stitched him up, at one point complaining to a nurse that "Christmas is the hardest time of the year. I'll bet we never even get a chance for a cup of coffee tonight."

Mikey remembered those words. He really never let much slip past him. So, the next afternoon, he did something he had never done before. Figuring that he had watched his mother and father often enough, Mikey tried his hand at making Cuban coffee. He poured the deep dark mix into the old thermos that his father frequently took to work and bicycled his way back to the hospital. He waited in the same emergency room until he spied his friend of the night before – Dr. Fred. "Here, doctor. This is for tonight and just in case." The young doc stood speechless – for one of the few times in his life. But it didn't really matter. Mikey was already out the door thinking to himself that he would explain and Papi would understand about the missing thermos.

Then it came. The morning of Christmas Eve. Mami explained: Be home, ready by 7:30. *Abuelita's* – Grandmother's – house. Noche Buena, roast pork and turkey and black beans and family and gifts, and *Misa del Gallo* – Midnight Mass – tradition....

But she did not explain – because she could not understand – the last day of freedom.

Mikey used it well. It seemed that he was everywhere: beaches and parks, and visiting friends, and well, just plain everywhere. Finally, in late afternoon, Mikey found himself peddling furiously. "Be home before Mami and Papi. Be ready – 7:30." He did not know just what time it was but it was getting late. As he peddled, he approached a young man – he looked like the gym coach at school – running along the side of the road and carrying a big old plastic bag over his shoulder.

"Where are you going, mister."

"To a meeting. And I'm gonna be late. This is heavier than I thought."

"What's in the bag?"

"You wouldn't believe it."

"Sure I would. What's in the bag?"

"A turkey and a ham."

"You're taking that to a meeting? Why?"

Mikey followed as the young runner trotted into a gas station and only sort of stopped at a water hose. Dousing himself over the head and still jogging in place, he began to explain.

"I'm going to a place just up the road. There's a lot of people who won't have any place to spend their Christmas Eve. No one wants them"

"Why," asked Mikey.

"Well. Most of us are alcoholics and drug addicts. They've hurt a lot of people. They've hurt themselves... but now they're — we're — trying real hard not to do that anymore. So, tonight we'll all just get together and help each other make it through tonight and tomorrow and not hurt ourselves or anyone else. And the ham and turkey are so we can all have a little bit of Christmas — even without family. A lot of us are bringing food and soda and we'll keep the doors open all night tonight and all day tomorrow. Just so that we can have someone around. Some kind of family — some kind of Christmas."

"Okay," said Mikey. "I understand. Here, let me carry the bag on my bike."

Mikey — despite the distance yet to be peddled — was home, and would you believe, dressed and groomed when his parents arrived. But it was already past his usual bed time when they reached Abuela's house. There was family and lots of food. There were gifts exchanged, although not many because no one really had a lot of money to spend on gifts, and besides, both his parents and los abuelos were still very traditional Cubans. The important gifts would wait for the Day of the Three Kings.

Late that night, the whole family — aunts and uncles, cousins and grandparents, Miguelito and his *padres* — walked the three blocks to the church.

Mikey really did not like this church. It was too big

and noisy, something like the school cafeteria when the third and fourth-graders all crammed inside. The statues were old and ugly. Besides, there wasn't ever a single Michael or Miguel represented by any of them. There were too many old ladies, in their mantijas or veils, with their faces caked in make-up and smelling of heavily perfumed powders. And the priests were even older than the statues.

They always talked about "in Cuba" and he had only learned where Cuba was this year in school. They only spoke in Spanish, and it wasn't even the Cuban-American Spanish that Miguelito understood.

But for now, on *Noche Buena* – Christmas Eve – he could no longer be Mikey. He was Miguel or Miguelito and after a day of bike peddling and exploring, after the dinner of roast pork, turkey, yams and yuca, after the walk to the church, Miguelito was very tired.

Nevertheless, he joined in, as best he could, singing the old Spanish songs before Mass. "It would be better," he thought to himself, "if they sing them in English like we do in school."

And he joined with others in laughing when suddenly the church's microphone system started to pick-up different radio stations and alternately play "Jingle Bells" and an announcement for the Sedano's market, together with the Spanish version of "We Wish You A Merry Christmas." Everything stopped in the church at this point, while men seemed to rush everywhere in a frantic attempt to fix the broken microphones.

When, at last, the troubles had been corrected — or at least everyone thought that was the case — Miguelito had already fallen fast asleep. He did not see or hear the priest come up the aisle. The music of the choir did not waken him. Mikey only began to stir as the priest, having finished the Gospel, approached the central aisle to begin his sermon and just as the microphone system again picked up the mysterious radio signals.

"What," asked the priest in his old and rumbling Spanish, "what is Christmas all about?" His voice seemed lost in the crackle of radio static and Christmas music and so, perhaps from frustration, perhaps for effect, he repeated himself. "Just what is Christmas all about?"

And, at precisely that moment, the microphone system seemed to die a quiet, natural death, as the radio announced, "Ask Mikey. He knows."

2008

The Lessons of the Flower Angel

There's a lot of background to this year's Christmas story.

First, since my father's death more than a decade ago, my family has been blessed by what some might call "a stalker." My mother, however, refers to him or her as "the Flower Angel." On every significant occasion — Christmas, New Years, their anniversary, mother's and daddy's birthdays, Easter, Fourth of July, Thanksgiving — flowers appear at Mom's front door, always with the same message: "For Mrs. Flynn in honor of Mr. Flynn" on scraps of paper, a torn envelop, a greeting card, a piece ripped from a grocery store paper bag. And always in a different handwriting.

Second, my mother has saved the report card proof that I once failed Religion. And the story about failing deportment and conduct — TRUE.

Finally, let me point out that one of my father's favorite priests and a special friend of mine recently participated in the unauthorized ordination of a woman priest. He has publicly advocated for the ordination of women as a matter of Justice and Rome has threatened to excommunicate him — something that will happen any day now, if it hasn't already. When Father Roy Bourgeois returned to Louisiana to inform his family of what he had done and Rome's reaction, he was moved to tears by the supportive response of his 92-year-old father, who said that Roy was doing what he thought was right and God would take care of them.

And so, with this background:

●●●●●●●●●●●

Mikey was in trouble. Big, big trouble. Just how much trouble was clear when his best friend, Roly, leaned over and whispered, "Wow, Mikey, are you in trouble now!"

Mikey was in trouble, so real, so big, so intense that the three pieces of paper and the envelope stapled to them that he carried in his back pack made him feel as though he were bearing the weight of the world on his shoulders.

He had been in trouble before, like the time in fifth grade when Sister Marie Anita — known in several states and on at least two continents (but never within her hearing distance) as "Attila the Nun" — flunked him in deportment and conduct. To make matters worse, she wrote a long explanation on his report card: "Talks constantly, cannot stay in his seat; always bothering other students by offering to help them with their class work." Now, two years later, Mikey still remembered his mother's reaction when, timorously, he presented her with that fatal document of doom. How, with one singular

movement that would have been the envy of any professional tennis players from Arthur Ashe, Jimmy Connors,
and Chrissy Everett to John McEnroe, Bjorn Borg and
Venus Williams, she swept her arm back to the dresser
beside her bed, grabbed her favorite hairbrush, and in a
perfect smashing forearm broke that hairbrush over his
rear end and uttered the most terrifying words of any
language: "If you think that's something........WAIT
'TIL YOUR FATHER GETS HOME."

Actually, *Papi* had been surprisingly nonplussed by
the report: "It just shows how smart he is," Papi said.
"He's bored. Maybe they need to teach him something
new." And so it was that Miguelito survived the Attack
of the Hun Nun. Survived, but never forgot.

But now. This new document. He already knew the
content of the envelop. It declared that not only would
he flunk religion — maybe for the year — but the ideas he
expressed on the attached pages were dangerously close
to heresy, and if he persisted in his erroneous thinking,
he might be expelled. He was not to return to school after the Christmas holiday without the letter — signed by
both parents — and presented to Sister Mary Paraclete,
known as "the parakeet" or *"la parajita."*

Like a would-be-great attorney, Mikey attempted
to plot — I mean plan — his defense. "It was a mistake."
Nope. That would never do; it was clearly his handwriting.

"I didn't mean it." Forget that one. He already knew what Papi would say: "If you didn't mean it, you shouldn't have written it."

"It didn't come out the way I meant it." Mami wouldn't buy that one for a minute. "Then you should have rewritten it."

He considered one defense after another. None would pass with his Little Havana jury.

"Chuck," thought Mikey. "That's it. I'll blame it all on Chuck."

And so, step-by-step, Mikey outlined his defense. It all started with Chuck, he'd tell Papi. (Papi might almost believe that.) Chuck read a report he did in sixth grade and told him he had the "potential to become a real wordsmith." A wordsmith. Fancy that: a wordsmith. "Of course," Chuck added, "you'll have to do a lot of reading and really develop a much more powerful vocabulary than you have now. Read, study good literature, pay attention, start thinking, watch The History Channel. Get an education; that's the secret to being a read wordsmith."

Mikey was convinced. He consumed vocabulary lists and crossword puzzles for children and whenever he was home the television was set to The History Channel, a development that pleased and puzzled his parents. And he wrote, and he wrote, and he wrote…. until he convinced himself that he was, indeed, a wordsmith.

That's it, Mikey decided. As his defense he would blame Chuck.

Of course, he'd also have to wait until just the right minute to spring his exonerating defense and alibi. But Mikey also knew he'd never get through the holiday break with this secret hanging over him. And, good news, tonight *Abuela* — grandmother — was cooking her coffee-can flan along with *ropa vieja and moros* — shredded beef and black beans and rice — and Papi would be in a good mood. It was going to be like pulling off a Band-Aid — the best way is quick, no sense dragging out the pain.

With his parents still *sobre mesa* (sitting at the table), the burnt caramel taste of Abuela's flan still at the back of their throat's, Mikey produced his own indictment: "I had a religion exam last week. Sister Parakeet, I mean Paraclete, didn't like my answer. I can't go back to school unless you sign the letter she wrote. But, it's not my fault… It's all Chuck's fault." The words gushed out.

Papi rolled back his chair. "Chuck, *quien es Chuck. No conosco a ningun Chuck.* Chuck. Who's Chuck. I don't know any Chuck."

"Sister Charles Borromeo,." Woops. First mistake. "I mean Sister Charles Borromeo. Some of the kids call her 'Chuck.'"

Mikey knew what he'd hear next even before he heard it: "Not in this house. If all the other kids jumped off the roof of the school, does that mean you'd jump off the roof. *Basta con Chuck. Y, ademas, como es que la Herma-na Charles es la responsible.* Enough with this Chuck stuff. And besides, how is it that Sister Charles is responsible for this."

"Because she told me to think. To read and listen and watch History Channel and to think for myself. So, when Sister Parakeet − I mean Sister Mary Paraclete − gave this exam, I did what Sister Charles told me to do: I thought for myself and wrote what I thought. Here, Papi, read it."

And Papi read first the question: "Name the different types of angels and describe how angels are involved in the Christmas story."

"Bien. Okay."

Then Mikey's answer:

"I don't believe in angels. If we consider the zeitgeist and the sits en lieben...."

Papi was already confused: *zeitgeist* and *sits en lieben?*

"The idea of heavenly creatures surrounding the throne of a supreme monarch was consistent with the experience of a cultural phenomenon in which powerful leaders were sur-rounded by sinecures and syncopates. Thus, angels around a heavenly throne of an all-powerful god.

"The Internet and Google and cut and paste are wonderful things, thought Mikey, his chest swollen with the pride of a wordsmith."

Papi was lost: "sinecures" and "syncopates." He

didn't know whether to stop and ask or pretend as though he understood.

So, he took the path of least resistance: "Miguel, explain to your mother what you are saying here.

"It's easy, Mami. Sister asked us about the angels at Christmas and I said that I don't believe in angels — at least not with wings and clouds and floating around God's throne. Those ideas come from a time when powerful kings, emperors, and dictators were always surrounded by Yes men — people who just did whatever they said to do and never questioned. And they all thought that, if God was the most powerful leader and up in heaven, then God had to have really special Yes men.

"On the History Channel I saw about Buddhists. They don't think Buddha is God and they have all kinds of Buddhas — laughing Buddhas, crying Buddhas, warrior Buddhas...

"You know how Father Mark keeps telling us that St. Francis said, 'Preach the Gospel all the time, with words when necessary'? And how he keeps saying that the angels were the first to preach the Gospel?

"In my test I said I didn't believe in churchy angels and statue angels... But I believe in angels that are more like Buddhas and what St. Francis said.

"Did you ever think that when Jesus was born and even though they didn't even have a place of their own to live in Mary and Joseph might have done something nice — something kind — for the owner of the stable or that they might have welcomed another homeless family into the stable. And they became angels — they went out and told the shepherds about Jesus and Mary and Joseph. That when the Wise Men came, Mary cooked for them and Joseph maybe gave up his bed for them — the way you make me give up my bed when Tio Jess comes to visit. And they went out and told the world the news of Jesus — the Wise Men Angels.

"There's all kinds of angels — we just never think of them that way. The Jewish nurse who works on Christmas so other nurses can spend time with their families. She's a nurse angel.

"The soldiers and Marines in Afghanistan and Iraq who are kind — who give candy or school books to kids or build schools for them or send them to America to have surgery to take care of wounds or birth defects. They're soldier and Marine angels.

"The kid in Tampa who died last year, and when Make A Wish asked him what he wanted, he said he wanted to build an orphanage for street kids in Nigeria. The orphanage builder angel. Or Tim Tebow from Florida, who won the Heisman Trophy and still goes on medical mission trips to help poor kids in Central America. The quarterback angel.

"The teacher who stays after to help a kid or who buys pencils and notebooks with her own money. She's a teacher angel.

"The lady who every month bakes cookies to send to soldiers and Marines in Afghanistan. The cookie angel.

"The cashier lady at Publix who smiles no matter how people treat her. The smiling angel.

"The cancer researcher angel, the children doctor angel, the teacher and coach angels.

"The man who gives blood every other month for the past twenty years because he has something special in his blood that they use for babies. Bleeder angels.

"Mother angels and father angels, foster parent angels. Adoptive parent angels. The gay man in Key West who adopted black foster children and gave them a safe and permanent home – The Gay Adopting Father Angel.

"See, Papi; see, Mamita… If the role of angels is to proclaim Good News of Great Joy… we don't need church and statue angels. We have angels of flesh and blood who preach the Good News every day, always… and never use words.

"So, I don't believe in angels because I believe in angels.

And Sister said that I flunked and that I can't come back to school until you've signed my test paper – the one with the F."

Papi said nothing. He pursed his lips, rubbed his forefinger and thumb just under his nose, and moved his chair away from the table. But, as he walked past him, he tussled Mikey's hair mumbling, "Miguelito, Migueli-to… Oh, Miguelito."

Saturday, Sunday, Monday, Tuesday… neither Papi nor Mamita mentioned Mikey's F or his paper or the letter from Sister Mary Parakeet (I mean Paraclete). Nothing was said all day on the twenty-fourth. But when he went to his room to dress for Noche Buena Mass Mikey spied his F paper on his bed. And, when he picked it up, he could hardly believe his eyes. It was covered with notes, in different colored inks and different penmanships, some strong and masculine, others delicate and feminine; some firm and vibrant, others with the telltale shakes of advanced age:

Felix Pascua y Prospero Ano Nuevo – Papi Angel

Merry Christmas, Sister. Happy New Year – Mami Angel

Happy New Year, Sister. – Abuela Angel

Felix Dia de los Tres Reyes Magos – Abuelo Angel.

And notes from *tios* and *tias angeles* – aunts and uncles angels.

Because, you see, we are called to be angels – to bring tidings of great joy to all the people, to proclaim, with words when necessary – in places great and small – in the most insignificant ways – today, every day that to us is born our Savior – Wonder Counselor, God Hero, Father Forever, Prince of Peace – Christ the Lord.

2011

Sebastian
The Christmas
Ibis

For weeks I've struggled with writing a short story that might deal with the great secrets and sacred mysteries of the Incarnation, of Christmas and God's choosing to become Man to consecrate and make holy our humanity. I'm sorry. No matter how hard or how long I've struggled, it didn't work out, especially since I had a theme that I just couldn't shake. And so...

There are two very special things you should know about my friend Miguelito. Well maybe three including his belief that Christmas is forever.

First, he loves ibi. Ibi? Is that right? Maybe? What's the plural of ibis? Okay. He loves ibises. His first baby pajamas were decorated with them; his first fluffy, stuffy toy was an ibis as big as he was; family lore is full of stories of trips to parks and how, barely a toddler, he stalked and chased them; and, when he was old enough to ride papi's shoulder's to football games he cheered for Sebastian and roared C-A-N-E-S with relish.

When others were fascinated by dinosaurs, he was exploring bird books. He knew that there were twenty-eight different kinds of ibises; that in one Egyptian pyramid they actually found more than one-and-a-half million ibis mummies; that it was one of the first birds on the ark and was released by Noah as a sign of fertility; that it is the symbol of the Israeli Special Forces; that it comes in black and white and speckled and scarlet and virtually every combination in between. He knew that it was a symbol of Wisdom and renowned for its bravery — the last bird to take shelter before a hurricane strikes and the first to reappear, although no one really knows where it goes to hide. And so, in his seven- and eight- and ten-year-old mind, the mighty ibis is the only one brave enough to meet storms head one.

Second, with uncles young enough to be cousins and

cousins older than some uncles, he long ago resolved the identity/title problem very simply: Everyone was *tio* — uncle. And having more tios than most kids could ever imagine gave him a unique perspective on life.

With dark brown, cocker-spaniel eyes and a shock of hair that falls accidentally — but looks intentionally — over his forehead, he's been called urchin, leprechaun, rag-a-muffin, rascal, hellion, rogue, and scamp. But he's never been called undecided or uncertain.

Through his uncles and almost forever, he's known that there are simple, great truths in life and a sure-and-certain-path that he would trod: Columbus High is for real men and Belen Jesuit Prep is for (he never quite knew what because tios would switch to Spanglish and mumble something that, he was told, he was "too young to hear"); if you're not big and strong enough to be quarterback, be a kicker — the other team will get a penalty if they even touch you; there are only two college football teams – the Hurricanes and everyone else; and he bleeds orange, green and white, although this one confused him because every time he got a nick or cut he only saw red.

Especially growing up in Miguelito's family, there is an advantage to so many uncles — their closest friends become adopted tios. So, when Tio Nick, to whom he had been attached shoulder to hip since he could barely stand, announced that he was moving three miles from home to a fraternity house at the University of Miami, every member of the family had an opinion and virtually every member of the family was part of the caravan moving his computer and flat screen, clothes, DVDs, George Forman grill and mattress and pillows. Abuela (Grandmother) even wanted to send the world's largest *arroz con pollo para esos muchachitos hambrientes* — chicken and rice for those hungry boys.

For Miguelito? His first reaction was that Tio's new world of brothers meant thirty-nine new tios. And, in typical Mikey fashion, he memorized the ride from Tio Nick's home — just two miles from his own: go past the Children's Hospital, which was almost next door, get to Red Road, go south and turn left. So easy that, before Nick had a chance to stretch out on his sofa or call any sorority girls, Mikey was back and... Well, to this day, Nick's not sure precisely what happened, whether Mikey staked a claim to the sofa or just assumed that what was Nick's was Mikey's. But... the rest, as they say, was history.

Sigma Chi brothers began supervising his homework; they insisted he play basketball with them and that he be on the sideline for intramural football and soccer. On Sundays — after church with the family, he was the ball boy when the beach volleyball court filled with screaming giggling girls for Spike For Mike — something about raising money for cancer, but Mikey really thought it was so that all his tios could "check out" the girls.

For Mikey, other than that he now claimed to have more uncles than any other ten-year-old in the world, one of the best parts of Nick's new home were the two brother-tios in the room next door. With blond hair, blue eyes and big stud-earrings in each ear, Tio Austin was six feet tall and a Miami Hurricanes cheerleader – just about the coolest thing that Mikey could ever imagine, except... Well, except for Tio Timmy who was actually – really, honest, to God – Sebastian. For Mikey, except for Nick, these two were *mas tios que nadie* – just simply the best uncles in the whole wide world. Especially when, at the start of each home football game, his tios – cheerleader and Sebastian – ran onto the field swinging four foot four inch, seventy-pound Mikey between them.

Now, I don't believe in coincidences. I like to say "Coincidences are minor miracles in which God chooses to remain anonymous while proving how much he loves and is with us." So, maybe it was just coincidence, but one afternoon while Mikey was finishing off his homework in the dining room, Nick and Timmy and Austin and Andy and Drew and five or six other Sigs wandered in to plan their Christmas charity. Put eight or ten Sigma Chis together to plan anything and you're sure to come up with fourteen or thirty-two different ideas. To a man, they couldn't agree with themselves.

I would be the last person in the world to tell you

that those youthful, testosterone-driven Sigma Chis had an exclusively positive influence on Mikey.

But it may well be that Mikey had as positive an influence on them as they might ever have had on him about school and sports – at least with regard to Christmas. And so, when, despite all their best efforts, the brothers couldn't decide on a single philanthropy – hey, that's a big word in fraternities – Mikey piped up with not one but two ideas: "Anonymous Christmas – don't tell anyone what you're doing, just do it 'cause it's a nice thing to do" and "Sebastian, the Christmas Ibis."

Whaaaa?

From childhood, Mikey had learned some simple lessons about Christmas: it was and is and will forever be God's gentle gift of kindness, the gift of a friend who will forever be with us, and those of us who receive that gentle gift are responsible for sharing it with others, especially those who are in need, in fear, and in pain; that we are called to share that Good News quietly, by simply being kind and doing the right thing because it is the right thing to do.

Sebastian, the Christmas Ibis? To Mikey, it all made sense. True friends, like the Ibis, are courageously with us in good times and bad. The Ibis was there at Christmas and remained faithful through the Cross and Resurrection. The Ibis was always there. He is the symbol of Wisdom – the understanding that God's love is forever present.

So, thanks to Mikey, there was no Christmas party at the house this year. Money for the party — which would have been illegal anyway 'cause the chapter was still on disciplinary probation — went instead to buying every stuffed ibis to be found anywhere in South Florida. Sebastian the Christmas Ibis "went viral." Stuffed Sebastians, large and small, began to appear everywhere — in boxes shipped to UM alumni in Afghanistan and on military bases around the world, on shelves and desks in the library and across campus with the note:

> "I'm Sebastian the Christmas Ibis.
> Please take me home or share me
> with someone else."

One morning, kids by the dozens at Miami Children's Hospital awoke to notes that read: "When you are afraid, please squeeze me for the gifts of Wisdom and Courage and know that I'll be here for you as long as you need. When you're not afraid anymore, please give me to someone who can share our Courage."

Overnight, police stations and squad cars were filled with Sebastians of all sizes as gifts for kids in trouble. In dialysis units and at Silvester Cancer Treatment Center; even in an old folks' home in Utah and a migrant labor camp in Mississippi. Sebastian went everywhere.

And after exams, when so many of his Sigma Chi tios scattered across the country, the eager mascot of so many uncles lived by their example, which explains why Sister Marie Anita (also known as "Atilla the Nun") expelled him from the Christmas choir for singing their version of *The Little Drummer Boy*:

> Said the shepherd boy to the mighty king,
> "Do you know what I know?"
> "I know a lot more." said the king,
> "because I went to college,
> I am smart and you're a silly fool
> Who didn't finish high school,
> who didn't finish high school…"

Mikey's tios cheered the news and high-fived him; his parents were less than pleased.

Having been excluded from the choir, Miguelito ended up with the best of the altar server jobs of Christmas Eve: Cross-bearer. Lead the procession in; lead the procession out. For the rest of the night, you get to hide out in the sacristy and — if you're really tired — catch a nap.

But not Mikey. Not this year. After exams, Sigs didn't just hit the highways and airport headed home, they abandoned two giant Santa bags of Sebastians, which Miquelito claimed for his own. And so, having secured them outside the sacristy door, once the procession was in, Miquelito toured the parking lot distributing Sebastian the Christmas Ibises to car windshields near and far. And, when that task was done he prepared the cross for the exit procession.

Forget the bright red ribbons and the poinsettia wreath with which Sister Carla had adorned the cross. They were so un-Miguelito. No, when, having lifted high the cross, at the end of the Mass, Mikey emerged from the sacristy, his abuelos, Mami and Papi, and most of the church could be heard gasping. But his tios cheered. Cheered a cross wrapped in orange, green and white and, at the foot of the cross, Sebastian the Christmas Ibis, a symbol of the Wisdom of the Love of God and the Courage to be Human.

Abuelo's Christmas Trees Miracle

A few weeks ago, as ordered by Mrs. Flynn, I began to put up Christmas decorations. First, the Christmas Crib. But, before the manger scene could be arranged, four large wooden butterflies atop the television cabinet had to be repositioned. The miracle of the butterflies — the earliest Christian symbol of our faith in the Resurrection - grabbed my imagination and has dominated my prayer life. Monarchs and blue

pansies and morphos. I grew up both uncon-
scious and profoundly aware of their incredible
complexity and wonderful simplicity.

With that in mind and credit to Henri Nouwen:

◄o►◄o►◄o►◄o►◄o►◄o►◄o►◄o►◄o►◄o►◄o►

From Thanksgivings 'til three o'clock Christmas Eve,
working in the little *ferretteria* — the neighborhood hard-
ware store — was family tradition. Three generations ago
Abuelo — grandfather — opened the store and sons and
daughters, grandsons and occasionally granddaughters
had put in their time in the parking lot selecting, demon-
strating, selling, cutting, tying and pulling, heaving and
squeezing Christmas trees into and onto every description of car, and each year pushing more than one or two
in grocery carts through neighborhoods and into every
conceivable sized apartment for *los ancianos* of the *vecin-
dad* — the elderly of the neighborhood. Each generation
put in their time and each had its stories. And all eventually learned and kept Abuelo's little gigantic secret: He
sold many of his trees at cost; in fact, more often than not
below cost because he knew that these neighbors would
never be able to afford the prices at Publix or Winn Dixie
or the Boys' Club.

"Ah, Señora Valdes," they would say, "Abuelo said
to tell you he has the perfect tree just for you. We have a

special cart. Can I walk it to your house?"

"Ah Señora Rodriguez, Abuelo picked this one out yesterday and said that you can settle with him in January."

"Ah Señora, Abuelo said this tree is too small; he can't sell it but he thinks it would be perfect for your apartment. He told me to deliver it for you. When would be a good time?"

"Ah, la familia Marquez. *Encantado verles* — good to see you. And Abuelo says, because the boys are getting bigger, they need a bigger tree this year and, guess what, he has some extra lights that he was certain you can use better than he can. Let's see if we can tie it to the top of your car. *Y abuelo dice Felix Navidad y Prospero Ano Nuevo* — and Abuelo says Merry Christmas and Happy New Year."

And while, by any reasonable account, Miquelito was still "way too young" — not to mention too small, he insisted that this was his year to share in a tradition he still did not fully understand. Now, truth be told, as he often did, Mikey had an ulterior motive. *Tio* — Uncle — Nick was working again this year, as he had been for the last five or six or seven; and Mikey would do just about anything to hang out with this most favorite of his cousins, who was, in fact, more than a decade older and so much bigger that, of course, he was an uncle in the hierarchy of Miguelitolandia — Michaelandia.

In fact, though half a generation separated them, their lives circled each other — like earth and moon casting regular eclipses. When Nick moved from home to his Sigma Chi Fraternity house, Mikey memorized the route and established his own after-school residence in the dining room turned study hall; when Mikey had a sporting event Nick and half the Sigs were there; a spelling bee or a baseball practice, Nick was tutor and coach. Because Nick liked sushi, Mikey decided it was his favorite food. It was, many observed, as if they often thought with the same mind.

And, although there is no proof of it because Nick would only have been ten or so when Mikey was born, it is family lore that Nick was the first member of the entire family to ever address Mikey in full sentences — real people talk: "Hey, Dude. Let go of the small stuff, no matter how big it seems; hold onto the big stuff no matter how small it seems. Forget happy. Choose Joy."

In fact, Nick counseled and disciplined Mikey with those words so often that they became part of the invisible glue bonding the two together — even though, from newborn 'til now as a strapping eleven-year-old, Mikey could never quite understand precisely what they meant. He had not the slightest idea of what Tio Nick was saying; he knew only that these words united them in a way that no one else in the family would ever understand.

Over time, as children and grandchildren grew — in

size and number, family Thanksgiving dinner gave way to a massive all-afternoon Sunday-after-Thanksgiving open-house. And now that all of the kids – including Mikey – understood the Spirit of Santa Claus the family introduced the practice of Secret Santas. It was practical, time-saving, and besides, with such a huge extended family, Abuela no longer had to spend September, October, and November shopping for everyone who might be on her list.

Now Mikey has been known as a scamp, scoundrel, charmer, flirt, thinker, hooligan, con artist, studious, and scheming to name but a few. And, as this year's self-appointed Director of Secret Santas, he put all of those attributes to work to uncover the secret meaning of "Dude. Let go of the small stuff, no matter how big it seems; hold onto the big stuff, no matter how small it seems. Forget happy. Choose Joy."

He had carefully written out the names of every family member – *tios* and *tias*, *primos* and *primas* – aunts and uncles and cousins so old they seemed like tios and tias – brothers, sisters, even boyfriends and girlfriends. Everyone's names went into the Secret Santa Bag. Everyone's except Mikey's. And that's where Miguelito's scamp-side came into play. He had already announced that he had drawn the name of his favorite cousin, and for Nick's draw, there was an absolutely identical bag with dozens of slips of paper all carrying but one name.

Then, on the Friday afternoon before Christmas, Mikey received a phone call. "Dude, bring your bike. We're gonna play hooky tomorrow. Don't worry. When no one's lookin' we'll stash your bike in my trunk and disappear. I've got your Christmas gift."

Now, it's almost impossible to describe the excitement of a kid when his favorite uncle-cousin proposes playing hooky and heading out on an adventure. But, true to his word, Nick arrived before opening on Saturday morning, and when the store reached a point of being so crowded that customers and family had to walk outside to find the space to change their minds, Nick gave Mikey a furtive raised eyebrow and a nod of the head toward a side door and they were gone.

There was something happily conspiratorial in the air as the two began their hooky adventure. So much fun that, until they arrived at the Sigma Chi House, neither spoke and both enjoyed the feeling of breaking a long list of unwritten rules. Pulling into the house, Nick broke the silence: "Duuuuude, long, hard ride or medium or easy? Your choice."

Truth was that Mikey was simply so happy to be with his tio-cousin that it didn't matter, and no matter how long or challenging the ride, he would never have admitted to difficulty or exhaustion; just being part of the adventure was enough. "Okay, Cuz. We'll make it short and sweet. We're headed to one of my favorite places but before you get your Christmas gift, it's time for you to 'fess up." And, with those words, Nick tossed his own bike into the back of the jeep and away they went. Mikey had a feeling his head would explode as he tried a hundred times over to understand "fess up."

"Fess up to what?"

And Nick wouldn't give him a break. He drove in silence, saying not a word and adding to Mikey's exploding sense that something had happened.

Fifteen minutes later, "We're here," announced Nick, pulling into a parking lot completely unknown to Mikey, and unloading their bikes. "Mount up."

Mikey followed Nick's lead as he chose a meandering path aside a low coral-rock wall. "Cuz, there's no place in town as special as this. It's the biggest garden you've ever seen and I want to give your Christmas gift but, first, you have to 'fess up."

Now Mikey's gut churned with a sense of being trapped and confused.

"Wanna tell me 'bout the Secret Santas or want me to tell you?," asked Nick with a smile as big as any that every graced the face of Santa Claus himself. "Don't worry," he said after what seemed like an endless pause. "I know that you rigged the Secret Santa. And, I think I've figured out precisely what to get you."

Mikey was on the verge of — well I'm not sure what he was on the verge of as he struggled with the idea of being caught by his hero tio – but, he was surely on the verge.

"How, how, how'd you know?" he stuttered.

Slowly, slowly the two biked the paths – to Mikey – but certainly not for Nick – with no destination in mind. A turn here, a curve there, a straight-a-way, another turn, a slow descent, and Nick stopped and dismounted. "Here," he said, looking out over a massive meadow filled with butterflies beyond counting. "This is my favorite place. A great place to think and talk and to give you your Christmas gift."

Nick was empty handed.

"Grab a sit, Cuz. Let's talk.

"Any idea how many times I've said to you '*No piensas en las cosas pequenas aunque grandes parecen; ahunta las cosas grandes aunque parecen pequenas! Olvidate de felicidad, escoje alegria!* Let go of the small stuff, no matter how big it seems; hold onto the big stuff, no matter how small it seems. Forget happy. Choose Joy!"

"Hundreds and hundreds," responded Mikey. "Every time you ever see me."

"For all the years you've been alive," added Nick, noting with confidence, "And for Christmas you really want me to explain 'cause you don't understand what it means. Right?"

"How'd you know," Mikey asked.

"Okay, here's the story. So many people are so busy

thinkin' and worryin' about, wantin' big things that they don't really understand that most of that stuff really isn't worth worrying about. They make the small stuff so big that it rules their lives.

"Look at this meadow… Most people would never ever stop here more than a minute. They'd be so busy thinkin' about the big stuff that they miss all the little stuff — the butterflies, the crabs, the view — that are really special.

"It's like Abuelo's Christmas trees. So many people are so worried about getting the biggest, the fullest, the just-right tree that they miss the important things. They worry about how much they cost, whether they're spruce or fir or Douglas. Do you know the secret of Abuelo's trees?

"What secret?" implored Miquelito.

"It's the secret of Abuelo's little trees. The ones nobody sees. The special ones for the Señoras Valdes and Rodriguez and the Familia Marquez and all those other trees we move around on old grocery carts. Every year those are the only ones they would ever have, if it weren't for Abuelo. He keeps them in a special corner. We're not supposed to show them to the folks with money. 'Cause they're in that corner, 'cause they are hidden away, almost everyone thinks they're little, scrawny, ugly trees. But — even though they're smaller than most, Abuelo picks each one out specially and he makes sure they're perfect and then we hide them in the corner. Abuelo thinks they're the most important trees of the year — because they were always for the people everyone else forgot."

Mikey's head wasn't quite spinning but he could feel himself filling with the pride of being allowed into a special secret world.

"People miss the little stuff that's really, really special. Dude, do you know the most important thing I own. Bet you'd never guess. At Christmas when you were in kindergarten, you gave me a drawing of you and me playing football. You made big crayon bars of every color and covered them with black crayon and then used a pencil to make the drawing. It's framed on the wall of my room. It's small and simple but it reminds me of the difference between happiness and joy. Happiness is just on the surface — it comes and goes and, for most people, it depends on everything outside themselves. Joy is deep and constant no matter what is happening around us.

"So, Mikey, now you're beginning to learn the lesson of Abuelo's Christmas trees. Just because everyone else thinks the big trees are the most important doesn't mean they are. For Abuelo it's the little trees and the little people who are most special. And for Abuelo these trees are part of the joy of Christmas.

"You see, Cuz, Joy is different from Happy. Abuelo teaches us that Joy is the most important reason for

Christmas – it's the way God shows himself to us. Abue-lo reminds us that the message of the Angels was 'joy to the world.' Joy is what happens when we know that we are deeply, deeply loved by God and others and that nothing – sickness, failure, problems, not even death – can take that love away.

"Your drawing on my wall is like Joy – under all that black crayon – is the picture of you and me together and nothing can break us up. All those bright colors, they're Joy."

"So, enjoy the butterflies. Enjoy my special place. My gift to you. Forget the little things, the small stuff that everyone else makes seem so important and big; hold onto the really important things that everyone else thinks are small and unimportant. Enjoy the secret of Abuelo's Christmas trees.

"And, for your gift to me, I only want one thing: Choose Joy. Choose Joy."

2007

The Christmas Safe Place

Miguelito hated math. It was a pure, perfect, uncomplicated, visceral — deep down in the guts - hate. It wasn't that he couldn't do it. In fact, he was actually pretty good at math. But math was just before gym — the dark before the dawn, the interminable drive forever marked by "are we there yet," the longest mile before summer's freedom of open fields and running and sunshine, the despair that ultimately could only lead to hope.

Miguelito hated math. In truth, he would do just about anything to avoid math. But, today, as Mikey bathed in the absolute totality of his loathing, delivery came in the form of terror of almost biblical proportions. With a quiet knock at the classroom door, Maria Victoria entered. Mikey didn't hate Maria Victoria — that might be a sin. He simply despised and detested her. Maria Victoria was Maria Victoria, never Maria or Vicki. Always Maria Victoria and she was a rat, a snitch. So, it might have been okay to hate her because *Papi* — Daddy — has always taught "The Lord hates a squealer" and hating her might not be sinful. But Maria Victoria delighted in snitching and getting every other fifth grader in trouble — whenever, wherever, and as often as possible. And she had that smirk on her face that told all the world she had a new victim. The note in her hand passed quickly to Mrs. Jason, the math teacher, and the announcement was made:

> Miguel Edwin
> Report to Sister Clare in the office
> immediately after math class.

No! Not now! Not at gym time! And NOT Sister Clare! His heart sank. There was no hope! He was condemned to the worst of all fates.

Two years ago, Father Reeves, the pastor, had imported a squadron of nuns – Carmelites – to run the parish school. And run it they did in strange brown and black habits, with veils and coifs and gimps. (Yes, gimps are actually part of some nuns' habits.)

When class ended, like a man long-condemned to an inevitable fate, Miguel trudged the seemingly mile-long terrazzo corridor to Sister Clare's office, reviewing in his mind all the possible charges for which he might be sentenced to the most horrific of all fates. He had not been involved in fights – at least not lately.

"Our Father, who art in Heaven…deliver us from evil…" he prayed in desperation even as he reviewed his conscience. He hadn't cheated, even at math – Papi would have kill him. He hadn't been involved in a food fight all year. And, it couldn't have been for having completely shaved his head in support of *Tia Isabel* – Aunt Isabel – when she lost her hair to chemotherapy. Papi had dealt with that issue two weeks earlier.

Then, barely having crossed the threshold of the office, Miguelito was brought up almost dead in his tracks by a fear he had never known before – Papi and his mother were in the principal's office. Talking with her. His fear knew no bounds.

"Ah, Miguel Edwin," Sister Clair called as she spied him through the slight opening in the door. "Come in, come in." Miquelito made his way into the principal's office, hardly taking notice of the two boys sitting ramrod straight and uncomfortable in the waiting room. And, even in the principal's office, as always and everywhere, he was greeted by Papi and his mother with tight, comforting *abrazos* — bear hugs — and quiet kisses to the crown of his bald head. For just a second, laughter almost overcame his fear as he imagined the principal's reaction to his bald-headed parents *besando* his equally bald head — a family move, Mami, Papi, *tios* and *primos* — uncles and aunts and cousins — all shaved bald in support of Tia Isabel.

"Miguel, thank you for joining us," Sister Clare began. "You're not in trouble, but your parents and I have a problem, and we don't want to make a decision without asking your help."

The boys in the waiting room, she explained, had only just arrived in Miami — without family, without friends. Their parents had smuggled them aboard a small boat that had landed only two days before on South Beach. Everyone else, including the boat's owner or pilot, had disappeared and the boys were found alone on the beach. They were angry and sad and frightened. They were alone and pained and, she said, they had, at six and eight years old, petulantly refused to say almost anything at all. Miguelito didn't quite understand what "petulantly" meant but the tone of her voice made it sound as though they were stubborn and probably just as determined as Miguelito could be.

"We're looking — Father Mark and I," Sister continued, "we're looking for a safe place for them to live, just through the holidays and until we can find something more permanent..."

"Miguel," Papi joined, "we won't decide without you."

Mikey's heart sank. He had long enjoyed his special role as the king of his castle. Number One Son. He was being asked to give up his throne. And at Christmas, when he was the embodiment of the *regalon* — the spoiled little prince.

He was caught — trapped by the spirit of Christmas, by the expectation of his YES so clear on his parents' faces, by the family history, so often repeated, of their own escape and immigrant history.

"Miguelito," Papi continued, "I know we're asking a lot from you, especially at Christmas, especially when you've never had to share your room or the house with anyone before. But, Miguelito, remember that Christmas depended on Kindness."

Mikey's heart hit bottom. And began to bounce back — at least a little. There could be no response to Papi. The story was a family tradition — Miguelito's First Christmas — how, with the newborn Miguel Edwin cradled in one arm, Papi had unwrapped each item of Abuela's Christmas manger and positioned each statue. How each year Papi would position the sheep and the donkeys and the cows inside the stable and then one by one move them outside, making room for the Mary and Joseph and their child swaddled and sheltered under the crèche's roof. How Papi had taught Mikey The Lesson of the Stable – that it was the home and the safe place of the cows and the sheep and donkeys, who had given up their home to make room for strangers. That Christmas depended on Kindness.

So, ten days before Christmas, Mikey and Mami and Papi walked out of the school office with two boat people-children and into a changed life for Mikey, who immediately took charge of the Cuban-Americanization of these strangers.

First, Mikey determined Vladamiroff and Gregoriano just wouldn't do for names. Even before reaching the parking lot, they had been "baptized" – albeit without water and outside the church – as Jess and Jake – good, solid South Florida names. Easy to remember and pure boy – each with just a touch of hellion.

By the time they reached home, Mikey was already planning – in rapid fire Spanglish: Mami and Papi would keep working; Abuela and Abuelo would take them shopping tomorrow to get clothes; on Monday they would start school even though there was only a week to go before the Christmas holiday; this weekend Mikey would show them everywhere and everything – he would borrow bikes from his best buddies Roly and

Brian; maybe they could be altar boys. Could they shave their heads, too? Oh, they hadn't yet met Tia Isabel; that's alright, we'll let them decide. How quickly could they learn English, what grades will they be in? For two kids who had, only hours earlier, been "boat people," the Cuban-Americanization of Jess and Jake took off like a flash.

While Mami and Papi and los abuelos, Father Mark and Sister Clare handled legal and immigration issues, Miguelito took charge of Jess and Jake. And it was a charge: charge here, charge there, charge into this adventure, charge into that; charge to los abuelos for *picadillo* — a Cuban specialty so good it doesn't translate — or a Cuban sandwich; charge to the homes of Mikey's friends so that Jess and Jake would have new and other friends. Sometimes it seemed as if they were charging just to charge. *Damn the torpedos, full steam ahead!*

But at night, with Jake trundled into Mikey's bed and Jess and Mikey on borrowed mattresses squeezed onto the floor, when the house was quiet, Jess and Jake spoke from the heart. How they missed their own mother and father, who had bravely trusted them to the man who brought them so far, only to abandon them on the beach; their mango tree and its sweet, golden fruit; school and friends — precious in any land and at any age; and their confidence that no matter how little they had, los abuelos in Cuba would always provide lunch or dinner and watch with pride as they downed every morsel, every last crumb and then with the dignity of their age and experience say to the boys *"perdonen lo poco que hay* – please excuse the little that there is, we wish there were more."

And, when stories and memories yielded to the exhaustion of the charge, Jess and Jake would quietly cry themselves to sleep – leaving Mikey profoundly affected by the honor of their tear-filled trust.

As the days sped by, one afternoon – just days before Christmas – Mikey, Jake and Jess found themselves alone in the house. And, encouraged by their experience of Mikey's complete openness and unending concern, the boys started asking questions. "Every day, whenever your family sits down for lunch or dinner, they pray. Why, to whom, what, what for? Christmas, Jesus, the crib by the tree? Why, when, how, what for?"

For the first time in his life, Mikey experienced a shift, a change, something suddenly different, even as he tried to explain. In the past, the answers that might have come would probably have been his mother's answers. Not now. He wasn't quite sure when the answers shifted, changed – maybe even grew. Maybe, just maybe it had been in Sister Clare's office – the look on Papi's face that said, "We do this, you do this because it is the right thing to do and in faith we do the right things because God calls us to do the right things – even when they're hard."

"I believe," said Mikey, actually feeling for the first

time the power of his own words, "I believe that God is love — the source, the power, the realness of love. And I believe that God is everywhere. And that wherever God is we are with him. So, I am with Mami and Papi right now, wherever they are — and they are with me just as much as I am with you. That God is here, and because He is also with your mother and father and your friends and your abuelos, they are also with you and you are with them — because God is everywhere and we are always with Him.

"Christmas, oh that's easy. I believe that long, long ago God loved us so much that, in a very special way, He wanted to be with us — to share our lives, to taste mangos and fly kites and ride bicycles and go fishing. And so, He chose — God chose — to be born a man — the son of Mary and Joseph."

Mikey was on his feet and shepherding his Wise Men (please pardon the mixed-metaphors) to the table on which, each year, Papi built the Christmas crib. "The story says that Joseph and his wife Mary had to travel far from their home — sort of like you guys — to the town of Bethlehem for a census."

Mikey covered his mouth in a conspiratorial whisper and noted, "I'm still not sure what a census is" before continuing.

"When they arrived in Bethlehem, there was no room for them in the inn ("I'm not quite sure what an inn is either," he admitted.) and they were forced to stay in the stable where the cows and sheep and donkeys stayed at night. And Mary wrapped her baby Jesus in pieces of cloth and placed him in a manger – that's the place where the animals ate – because it was filled with straw and was more comfortable for the baby than making him sleep on the floor."

Now Mikey was going to share a family secret. Well, it really wasn't a secret – more of a family story. "My abuelos and Mami say that when I was a baby Papi held me in his arms as he put together this little stable. First he put up the walls and put on the roof; then he put all the cows and donkeys and sheep inside because, he said, the stable was really theirs. It was their warm safe space. Then, Papi asked the cows and donkeys and the sheep if it was okay, if they would mind that Mary and Joseph and the Baby Jesus stayed there – in their stable, where it was warm and safe. Papi would only place the Virgin and Joseph and the Baby Jesus in the stable when the cows and donkeys and sheep have given their permission.

"Each year ever since, Papi does the same thing – he asks permission for Mary and Joseph and their Baby to enter the stable. And he reminds us that Christmas happens because of Kindness – God's Kindness to us and the Kindness of the animals who gave up the warmth of their stable."

He paused for a moment – perhaps for dramatic effect, perhaps because he was finally beginning to understand that the family story was so much more – not just a story but a lesson of Christmas, a lesson of Life. At last, "Okay, time for Abuela's. She's made dinner and Mami and Papi will be there soon," he said.

Two days later, the two Little Wise Men from Cuba joined Mikey and Mami and Papi and abuelos and tios and tias and primos for the *Misa del Gallo* – Christmas Eve Mass. Jess and Jake understood little and spent much of the Mass thinking about the *lechon* – whole roast pig over which they had labored with Tio Ricky through much of the day, building the pit, spreading the hot coals and preparing blankets of banana leaves. They gazed in wonder as Mikey, resplendent in his red cassock and starched white surplice, held high the cross and led the procession of servers, readers, and priests. They dozed through the sermon and sat strangely, sadly alone for a moment as the entire family went forward to receive the Body of Christ. But for both – for Jess and Jake – there was a mysterious, deep-in-the-heart feeling of warmth and safety. And when Mass was over, as the family prepared for the three-block walk back home, Jess whispered in Miguelito's ear, "Please, Miguelito, could you get the key and open the door for us before anyone – before everyone – gets home."

Mikey didn't understand; he only knew it was important. And, with keys borrowed from Papi in hand, the Three Wise Men (including one from *la Pequena Havana* — Little Havana) ran home.

"No, Miquel. You can't come in. Only a minute. There's something we have to do," Jess insisted as he and Jake slid through the door, shutting it securely behind them, only to reemerge but seconds later.

Lechon, gifts, laughter, stories, yawns, dirty dishes, Good Nights and *Felix Navidades*, the evening passed as it had all of Mikey's years. He gave no further thought to the request of Jess and Jake. He never discovered why they had gone inside.

But late that night, very early Christmas morning, when all of the guests had left, when gifts had been retrieved from their hiding places and Santa Claus's milk had been drunk and his cookies eaten — and their plate and glass left precisely where they had been before the boys went off to dream — and dishes were safely secured in the dishwasher that quietly hummed its early morning tune, Papi made one final tour of the house — checking doors, turning off lights.

As was his custom, the last lights to be extinguished were those of the Christmas tree. Stopping for a moment to reflect, he noticed — there on the table beside the tree something was just ever so slightly amiss. The Christmas stable had been... not just changed but crowded. Between the walls, under the roof, for the first time —

Mary, Joseph, and the Christ Child shared the stable with the donkeys and the sheep and the cows. The two Wise Men from the South had moved all the figures together — sharing the safety and warmth of the Stable. For Christmas happens because of Kindness.

1999

Super-Important Jobs

The day after Thanksgiving was not supposed to be "The Guys Day Out" but it was, and therein lies our Christmas Meditation.

◄○►◄○►◄○►◄○►◄○►◄○►◄○►◄○►◄○►◄○►

The year and the millennium were not ending well. The precipitous slide into disaster started just after breakfast on October 17. Michael — he no longer called himself "Mikey" and completely eschewed "Miguelito" — casually asked his mother for a stamp... for a letter... to God... with a question... about Halloween.

> Dear God,
> Ever since I can remember, my Tía and my Abuela have called me a 'Little Devil.' So, I was thinking that I would dress-up as a devil this year for Halloween. Of course, that is if it's okay with you. I know that You are very busy. So, if I don't get an answer, I'll assume it's alright.
> Sincerely, Michael.

Abuela was outraged. Between *"Madre de Dioses"* and crossing herself, she was practically speechless right up to the night that Michael, red tail in one hand, trick-or-treat bag in the other, went down the street.

Having survived "the shame" and "What would the neighbors think?" Abuela began her "November mantra." Something of a tribute to her *Cubanidad* — Cubanness — and her American citizenship. "A good turkey means a good pig. I take care of the turkey and *El Viejo* — the 'Old Man" — Michael's *abuelo* — grandfather — will take care of the pig." She started repeating it over and over beginning the day after Halloween, and as

Thanksgiving approached, her mantra rose to almost fevered pitch. It was as if this Cuban-American prayer could ensure good holidays. Then the prayer changed – from hopeful supplication to confident exasperation: "I'll take care of the turkey *pero ese viejo* – but that old man – God only knows what he'll do with the pig."

It had become a family tradition. As Abuela trumpeted her assurances about the turkey and bemoaned her discomfort about the Old Man's Christmas pig, daughters and daughters-in-law clucked their empathic understanding, and sons and sons-in-law struggled mightily to contain their snickers.

At the appointed hour, with the entire family seated and the dining room table laden with all the trimmings, Abuela presented her turkey. Golden, crisp, big enough to feed the entire Miami Hurricanes football team. "*Perdonen lo poco que hay,*" she said, beaming with pride and confidence, "Pardon the little that there is; I don't think it's as good as last year. Maybe I cooked it too long, maybe dry."

Of course, the turkey was anything but dry and dinner, as usual, was spectacular. In family fashion, everyone had a great time. Conversation ranged from a cousin's football game the next day to who would get what for Christmas. There was laughter aplenty and not only were children seen but they were also heard. All, that is, but Michael, who didn't say a word until, as he finished his second piece of apple pie, announced, "I'm not going to be an altar boy this year and I'm not going to be an angel. I hate it when the *viejas* – the old ladies – pinch my cheeks and tell me that I'm *'un angelito precioso'* – 'a precious little angel' – and how much I've grown." Then, pushing his plate aside, he calmly rose and asked, "May I be excused, please."

You could have knocked the entire gathering to the floor with a feather. It was rumored for days afterwards that Abuela grabbed her chest whispering "*mi corazon, mi corazon* – my heart, my heart." Whether she did or not, Michael's mother turned to his father and said something about "your son," and more than one teenage cousin cheered under his breath "Way to go, Mikey!"

Whatever the response, Michael's declaration brought Thanksgiving to a thundering halt. The ladies adjourned to the kitchen to commiserate with each and do the dishes, while Abuela blamed "el viejo" for putting ideas in Michael's mind. "And, if he thinks I'm going shopping for a tree with him tomorrow just so that he can shout at me, well, he's got another thing coming," Abuela declared in a voice loud enough to be heard throughout the house.

For as long as anyone could remember Abuela and Abuelo had had the same Day-After-Thanksgiving fight. With Miguelito in tow and on their way to one old Cuban parish or another, Abuelo would tell her not to say a word about any tree that she liked – "Those American Red Necks will beat you up on the price if they think you like a tree. You must always say that it is puny, missing branches, find something wrong with it, and then bargain," he told her. And, year after year, each time she saw a tree she liked Abuela announced to the world, "*Ay, que lindo. Este a mi me gusta.* This one's beautiful. I love it." And Abuelo would complain all the way to New Year that because she could not keep quiet the tree had cost him way too much.

"No, he can go buy the tree all by himself. Tomorrow we go shopping – it's the Ladies' Day.," she declared. "We go shopping and he…"

And so, the Day After Thanksgiving became a Guys' Thing. Michael's father woke him early, "Come on, guy, we have lots to do today." And, after breakfast, he announced," We're going Christmas tree shopping this year."

Mikey started to protest about Abuelo and Abuela, but his father would have not a word of it, and, instead of driving to San Juan Bosco or Immaculate Conception or Divine Providence, where the grandparents ALWAYS bought their trees, this time they went down US1 to the Fire Station and they bought four Christmas trees for their own home, for both sets of grandparents, and for Mrs. Rodriguez, whose husband died three years ago.

And, when all four trees had been loaded into and

on top of the car, they kept driving SOUTH. To "some place special for lunch, a place where really important decisions are made," Michael's father explained. Just past the University they took a sharp right and then his father made a wild U-turn and traveled down a back road, "It's called Bill And Ted's — I started coming here in college. Everyone I know has been here. We've solved most of the world's problems over a couple of cheeseburgers and a pitcher of um, ah, aaaah sodas."

"So, Michael," Papi began, "this Altar Boy and Angel decision?" He was neither condescending or demanding; he wanted to understand.

"Well, when I'm an altar boy all the viejas — the little old ladies — pinch my cheeks and tell me how much I've grown. And when I'm an angel they pinch my cheeks and tell me how cute I am. No more. It hurts and it's embarrassing. Besides, I'm not sure there really are angels — at least not with wings and halos."

Michael had the two elements of a perfect argument — reason and doubt.

"Okay, Michael. I respect your position. The decision is yours. But, before you decide, you have to consider my arguments.

"First, many of those viejas have no one. Pinching your cheeks and telling you what they do will give them something to smile and talk about for weeks. Angels have a job — to announce to the world that God loves us and that at Christmas He becomes a man like us to show us His love. Giving old ladies something to smile about is just one way that angels announce God's love.

"Truth is, Mikey, I kinda doubt the wings and halo bit, too.

"But I believe that there are angels. When you were so sick in August the doctors and nurses were angels. Only God could give them so much knowledge as a sign of how much he loves us.

"Good friends who stand by us in difficult times, they're angels announcing to us that, through them, God loves us. Mikey, there are angels everywhere. You see them and talk to them, and if you listen carefully, they tell us that God loves us in all kinds of ways.

"But my favorite angel is the Flower Angel."

Mikey didn't understand this and so his father continued, "You know Mrs. Rodriguez. We just bought a tree for her. Well, ever since Mr. Rodriguez died three years ago, on every special occasion – Christmas, Easter, Memorial Day, Thanksgiving, her birthday, his birthday, their anniversary, the Fourth of July, the anniversary of his death – someone leaves flowers at her front door. It's not me; I don't know who it is; no one has figured it out. Always the same note: 'For Mrs. Rodriguez in Honor of Mr. Rodriguez.'

"But here's the mystery, every note has been in a different handwriting and almost every time the flowers have been delivered while Mrs. Rodriguez was at home.

"Of course, your mother thought that it was spooky and wanted to call the police. But Mrs. Rodriguez says they come from 'The Flower Angel.'

"The way I see it, son, angels only had two Super-Important jobs — to announce Christmas and to announce the Resurrection of Jesus. After that, angels simply tell us that God loves us and that's a job that all of us can do.

"That's why I brought you here. Lots of important decisions have been made at Bill and Ted's and this is the first important decision you have to make: To angel on Christmas Eve or not to angel. But there's a second important decision: To spend the rest of your life being an angel to all kinds of people in all kinds of situations — to let them know how much God loves them — or not.

"Okay, finish up. Let's get this show on the road."

◄o►◄o►◄o►◄o►◄o►◄o►◄o►◄o►◄o►◄o►◄o►

I don't know what decision Miguelito made. Midnight Mass at San Juan Bosco will start in a little while. If you want to go and see for yourself....

2005

$\mathcal{B}$roken Statues, Broken Hearts

$\mathbf{M}$uch has happened since last we gathered.

In the days right after Hurricane Katrina, the St. Francis of Assisi statue in Mom's backyard "lost its head" — the effect of years of sun, wind, and rain. When I began decorating our Christmas tree, I discovered that one of my mother's Christmas Angels had also lost his head. Because I'm always blamed for anything that goes wrong, I loudly and immediately voiced my dismay — hoping to deflect any responsibility. Fortunately, in the days that followed and as she attempted to Elmer's glue the statue together, Mom discovered telltale traces of old glue. I was exonerated before I could be blamed.

But these celestial decapitations left me thinking about this evening's homily.

◄o►◄o►◄o►◄o►◄o►◄o►◄o►◄o►◄o►◄o►◄o►

It wasn't until just before Christmas that Mark truly began to appreciate just how much the Church of his youth had changed. It wasn't the language of the Mass or the Sisters in "civilian clothes" or any of the other trappings of change that always make the press. He accepted them as being as much a part of life as breathing and prayer.

No, the change was encapsulated in one simple reality: Over the past year, old-age and its consequences had decimated the Altar Society. Essentially, "the *damas*," − "the ladies" − as he called them, were no more. But, like most of us, he had not really thought about them until he needed them and they were no longer there − claimed by illness or death (he had anointed and buried them) or children who had moved them into the grandparents' wings of McMansions in Kendall and Pinecrest.

But with less than two weeks before Christmas, Mark suddenly realized that there were no poinsettias or Christmas trees in the sanctuary and he neither knew where the Christmas crib and its statues were hidden nor did he have the time or inclination for such a project.

So, in an unthinking flash he made an executive/pastoral decision: Call Sister at the school, make it a class project, include a couple of altar boys (they always know where everything is hidden), let the kids handle it all.

He didn't think about it again – done, *fini, se acabo la cosa* – until last Monday. It was a great morning, clear blue skies, perfect temperature, humidity just right. He grabbed a fistful of test responses from grade school religion exams, a couple of books and his laptop, and with coffee mug in hand settled down in his not-so-secret get-away office in the rear of the sacristy to work on his Christmas homily.

The kids' tests were great material:
- The first book of the Bible is called the Book of Guinessis.
- Lot's wife was a pillar of salt during the day but a ball of fire during the night.
- The Jews were a proud people and throughout history they had trouble with unsympathetic genitals.
- Moses led the Jews through the Red Sea where they made unleavened bread which is bread

made without any ingredients
- The Seventh Commandment is "Thou shalt not admit adultery."
- The greatest miracle in the Bible is when Joshua told his son to stand still and he obeyed him.
- Jesus was born because Mary had an immaculate contraction and the Three Wise Guys arrived from the East Side to visit him.
- St. John the Blacksmith dumped water on his head.
- St. Paul cavorted to Christianity and he preached holy acrimony, which is another name for marriage.
- Christians have only one spouse. This is called monotony.

"I'll use the Jesus and some of the marriage stuff," Mark told himself, turning to the theological points he wanted to make on Christmas Eve.

Things were moving smoothly, he had determined his intro and bullet-pointed his critical issues when his productive quiet was shattered by children's screams.

"Ooohhhh, my arm. My arm's broken."

"My finger… Look what happened to my finger."

"Oh no. I'm losing my head."

"Help me, someone broke my legs…. What am I going to do?"

He'd have run in the direction of the pain-filled screams and groans if they hadn't been interspersed with outbursts of youthful laughs and a pervasive sense that this was more about fun than it was about the seriousness of shattered limbs and broken bones.

As much as he wanted to finish the task at hand, the laughter and faked pain slowly worked their way into and destroyed his concentration, leaving him no choice but to pursue the voices, which were clearly coming from the sanctuary, and to understand what was happening.

Rather than walk right onto the altar, he held back just a little, capturing a full sense of the chaos of eight or nine pre-teens preparing the altar's manger scene. He'd probably have returned to his books, leaving the kids to their own devices, had he not, with a sinking feeling of fear mixed with panic, recognized that the munchkin mob was under the immediate direction of none-other-than Miquelito.

Mark quietly edged into the sanctuary, seating himself in the closest possible chair and watched the goings-on. The more he watched the more he realized three things: the kids had established the largest collection of Christmas crib statuary he had ever seen; few – if any – of the elements matched; and, from a distance, it appeared that all were injured – cracks and chips in halos, sun faded clothing, missing fingers, arms, and legs.

134

Had he thought about it, he would have kept his silence but before he could catch himself, Mark was asking, "Mikey, what's happening?"

All eyes turned to Mark.

"We're just putting the Christmas crib together," Michael answered, looking up from amidst a mob of plaster-of-paris, plastic and wooden shepherds, Wise Men and stable creatures, Josephs and Marys and Baby Jesuses ranging in size from fit-in-the-palm-of-your-hand to "If he were real he could play linebacker for the Miami Hurricanes" big.

"But, Mikey, where'd you get all these things?" Mark asked.

"Sister said we could make our own crib; we had an election and I was voted to be the captain and we decided to do something different…"

Mark felt himself losing control. He didn't know where to look first and he wasn't quite sure what the expression on his face was saying. Mikey, for his part, was pretty sure that Father just might explode at any second. So, he just kept talking — faster and faster. "Did you know that twenty-five years ago some American Sisters were killed in El Salvador just because they worked with the poor. One of them wrote about how Jesus came to help mend broken hearts and heal people who are sad and suffering. She said that Jesus wants us to find him in the world and people around us, to heal their wounds and make our world better.

"We started thinking that Christmas is really for broken people... Mary and Joseph were strangers — homeless; the manger wasn't a nice, neat, clean place for a baby — it's where the cows and donkeys ate their hay. It was disgusting."

Now Emma joined in and Mark was being lectured by sixth graders. "The shepherds were the poorest people in Israel, nobody wanted to even be around them," she said. "And, the Wise Men were the Haitians and the Salvadorians and the Guatemalans of His time — they were people who came from foreign lands, who spoke strange languages and had strange customs."

Mark knew he was in for a "Theology of Incarnation 101" lesson and was already mentally tearing up the last hour's homily notes. His choices were simple: stick with heavy duty theology or learn from the kids and go with the flow of their insights. Mustering all of his pastoral courage, he settled into the chaos.

"We started thinking how many broken people we know," said Mikey. "All the viejas — the old ladies who don't have families anymore, who no one visits." The major munchkins moved in to join the lesson and were beginning to add their own examples of the broken — a classmate whose father was physically and emotionally abusive and who tried to spend as much time away from home as possible, a secret the boy struggled to keep but his best friends knew and respected; a teacher whose husband had cancer; people who are alcoholic and drug addicted; all those in New Orleans and everywhere else who've lost their homes…

"My brother's in Iraq with the Marines and my mother worries all day long," said Jimmy.

"My cousin was killed in Afghanistan two years ago and his mother doesn't even want to have Christmas," chimed Fred.

It was the beginning of a litany of intentions and broken souls — the tsunami in Japan and the earthquake in Pakistan.

The kids knew the human condition and they embraced it. All the sick at Miami Children's Hospital ("We make Christmas and Valentines cards for them so they don't feel forgotten"), doctors and nurses and firemen and police, and teachers, and women who suffer the emotional pain of their abortions, and single parents, especially those in the military in Iraq and Afghanistan. People around the world who are killed in the defense of human rights like Sister Dorothy Stang who was murdered in Brazil, and the rape victims of Darfur in the Sudan.

Finally, Team Captain Miguelito stood, as if to signal the end of the litany. "You see, Father, when we started thinking about it, we realized that the Sisters were right. Christmas is about Jesus coming to bind up the wounds of the souls of God's people and we're supposed to be part of that. It's why He came and what we have to do.

"The crib that the viejas put up is pretty but it's not the way Christmas was or what it's really all about.

"We started looking around. Do you have any idea how many broken statues people have? Not just old *Lazaros* and *Santa Barbaras*, but shepherds and Wise Men and Josephs and Marys. And *voila!*"

The "*Voila*" was a little much, even for Mikey. Mark bite his lip to control the grin that would betray the seriousness of the moment.

"We decided to do a Christmas manger that speaks about all those who are broken and reminds people that they − that we − must heal them," Miguelito was finished and Mark was left with much to think about.

So it was that at Saturday's Christmas Eve Mass, having finished proclaiming the Gospel, Mark walked to the center of the sanctuary to view once more the hodge-podge, almost cacophonous jumble of stable figures − missing fingers, broken arms, chipped halos, and cracked tunics. He then moved to the center of the main aisle, quietly put his finger tips to his mouth, pawed a few times at the ground, and slowly − almost sheepishly − looked up.

"Merry Christmas," he began. "I guess you've seen our rather unique Christmas manger scene. Let me, please, share with you the theology of a Maryknoll Sister who died twenty-five years ago in El Salvador and the wisdom of your children…

"The following was written by Sister Carla Piette, M.M., who died in 1980 while trying to help a former political prisoner return to his family. Together with the decapitated St. Francis and Christmas Angel, it was the inspiration for this year's Christmas homily. Please take it home with you, read it every now and then and pray and think…

The Lord has guided me so far.
And in His guidance he has up and dropped me here…
at this time and in this place in history.
To search for and find Him.
Not somewhere else.
But here.
And so HERE I WILL STAY.
until I have found that broken Lord, in all His forms
and all His various pieces,
until I have completely bound-up his wounds
and covered His whole Body, His People
with the rich oil of gladness

And when that has been done,
He will up and drop me again —
Either into His promised Kingdom,
or into the midst
of another jigsaw puzzle of
His broken body, His hurting People.

Maryknoll Sister Carla Piette
Santiago, Chile - August 5, 1977

2001

My Prayer

Last week, having set out on a little pastoral mission, I ended-up caught in traffic for over an hour-and-a-half. For some reason, I began to reflect on the call of the prophet Elijah.

You may recall that, filled with fear because the people had put other prophets to the sword and were threatening to kill him, Elijah ran off and hid in a cave. We are told that when the Lord approached him, there was first a mighty hurricane that split the mountains and scattered the rocks, but the Lord was not in the hurricane. And then an earthquake and fire, but the Lord was not in the earthquake or the fire. Then came "a still, small voice, as if a gentle breeze, and the Lord was in the breeze."

Mark Reeves, who has celebrated many of Christmas Eve liturgies with us, will be ordained to the priesthood in May. Mark is so conservative that I keep telling him he has to "loosen up, get a little radical." For months, I've wondered what would happen if Mark met our Christmas friend Miguelito. So, in part, tonight's homily is a celebration of the wonderful gift of priesthood that you – the People of God – will soon share with Mark.

◄◦►◄◦►◄◦►◄◦►◄◦►◄◦►◄◦►◄◦►◄◦►◄◦►◄◦►

It was Father Mark's first assignment.

The parish was old – average age when you factored out the school kids – was just past death. The population – almost entirely immigrants from more countries than there are United Nations delegations. The parish team consisted of three other priests – all in their 60s, four Sisters of Our Lady of Perpetual Pain and Disappointment and three retired Maryknoll nuns from the Philippines and Guatemala who had more energy than the other seven combined. The church – pre-Last Supper. And the sanctuary was so cluttered that Mark, who was decidedly a minimalist in every aspect of his life, feared it would force him to need major anti-psychotic medications. In short, Mark could only tell himself that this assignment was God's retribution for some long-forgotten but obviously very serious early-life sin.

Over time, he accomplished a few things. Chairs, kneelers, and other clutter disappeared from the church, only to be resurrected in a little-known private antiques dealership in north Broward, with the proceeds going to a badly under-equipped summer baseball league and an AIDS program.

So it was that, as the first Sunday of Advent approached, Mark hit on a deal. He leased out a small section of the church parking lot to a Christmas tree seller. A simple arrangement – no cost to the dealer, who would sell the runts of his litter at guaranteed lower prices to the parishioners, most of whom would lug their small trees home in "borrowed" grocery store carts; and the parish would get eight big trees at cost for the altar. And, he had decided, "I'll get the altar servers to decorate them. It will add some child-likeness to the celebration. Whoever does the best job gets to choose which Mass he will serve at Christmas."

He announced the competition at the first servers' meeting of December. It was well received – a great idea. Only one question from Miguelito: "Can we work as a team?"

"Of course," he said, never dreaming of the consequences of those two small words.

He was proud of himself. But not everyone was as enthusiastic about the idea. It certainly wasn't going over too well with the Sisters of Eternal Misery and Unending Sorrow.

"Well, I never," harrumphed Sister Icebergia so many times that he began to think to himself, "Well, maybe you ought to."

Nonetheless, the Maryknoll Sisters seemed to enjoy the process and kept telling him how excited the altar servers were and what a great idea it was.

Maryknoll Sister Theresa assured him that the preparations were going well. "Primitively," she said. "But well. Lots of lights and colored paper chains. It's not 'Needless Mark-up' (her favorite name for Neiman Marcus) or Macy's but it's going well and the kids are into it."

"It'll bring some spirit to the place," said Maryknoll Sister Consu.

"Let the kids have a good time and do something that's meaningful for them," added Helen. "Forget about us old folks." Mark thought, but could not be certain, she had actually said "old farts."

"But," noted Consu and Theresa, almost in unison one afternoon. "We have no idea what your buddy Miguelito is doing. We don't see him much and when we do, he just keeps saying, 'We're working on it. You'll see.'"

"Of course," Helen added, in a conspiratorial whisper, "I'm worried about Miquelito. He's been hanging with some new kids. I don't even think they are Catholic. And he just keeps saying that you said that they could work in teams and he has his team."

On the Third Sunday of Advent, after the noon Mass and since there was time because the Dolphins weren't playing (and losing) until later that afternoon, Mark asked Chief Altar Server Michael — a.k.a. Miguel and Miguelito — "How's your tree going, Mickey? What's happening with your team? Who's on your team, anyway?"

"Great. Some friends of mine. New kids. You don't know them — yet!" Mickey was almost out the door before the priest realized that the answers had come in fewer words than he had used for the questions.

"Wait, Miquelito! I know all the altar servers. There are no new kids."

"Got to go, It's Eid Feast and Hanukah, Father"

"Woooowww, Michael. Slow down. Tell me more."

"Father," said Michael. "You said we could work in teams. You didn't say who had to be on our teams."

Mark could already feel the noose of his own words tightening around his neck.

"So my team is Hiam Levy and...."

"Who????" The priest could already hear the phone call from the Archbishop's Office.

"They're new. Hiam's family is Jewish from Cuba. They just got here in August. He lives next door. Ben's family is from Bangladesh. His mother is a doctor and his father was a college professor but they don't do that anymore. They got relocated by some refugee group. They live in the house in back of *Abuela's*" — Mikey's grandmother."

It was, Mark realized, another one of those incredible but true "Tales from the World of Miguelito." Those adventures that one never tried to analyze or understand but just went along enjoying the ride.

"So," the boy continued, "we're celebrating December of Eating Good. There's Hanukkah, and then the Eid Feast with the Muslims to end the fast of Ramadan, and then we're going to decorate the Christmas tree and you said that any team that wins can choose whatever Mass it wants to be altar servers and we've already decided that we are going to do Christmas morning at eight o'clock so that all the other kids can sleep or play with their presents."

And, when the judges decision was announced, they did win, helped out in no small measure by the fact that the Maryknoll Sisters Theresa and Consu and Helen out voted Sisters Icebergia and Carela de Ville of the Sisters of Sour Grapes.

"It's a masterpiece of the Christmas message," explained Theresa. "The symbols of every major religion in the world, flags of more countries than I can name, and the word 'Peace' in a constant streamer in all kinds of languages."

On cue from Miguelito, and in unison, the three designers announced, "It's called the Holy Immigrants Tree."

The ringleader explained, "It tells us that we are all children of God and brothers and sisters to each other; it reminds us that the Holy Family were immigrants — homeless, desperate, alone, at the mercy of strangers, and it speaks for us the greeting of the angels and the promise of Christmas — that Jesus came as Prince of Peace."

With reasoning like that how could the Jew from Cuba, the Muslim from Bangladesh, and the Catholic from Little Havana not win?

True to his word, Miguelito chose to serve Christmas morning eight a.m. mass so that other kids could sleep or play with their toys.

And, as Father Mark processed up the aisle, behind the cross-bearing Cuban-American Catholic altar boy from Little Havana, the Jewish political refugee from Havana with his smoking incenser, and the recently arrived Bangladeshi Muslim carrying the Book of the Gospels, he thought, "I'm not even ordained seven months and I'll be causing the Archbishop's next heart attack when he hears about this one. For this, I gave up law?"

But, as he approached the altar, he saw again the PEACE streamer. And he remembered the call of the Prophet — "And the Word of the Lord came in the gentle breeze, as if a whisper."

◄O►◄O►◄O►◄O►◄O►◄O►◄O►◄O►◄O►◄O►◄O►

My prayer for you this Christmas is that you be able to hear the Word of the Lord, the Word that whispers "Peace." To hear it as I have:

In parents and brothers and sister, in family and friends who have taught the values of hospitality and the enduring Faith that is Christmas and Hope.

In the voices of Billy and Jennie Mullowney as they speak about their twins, Will and Laurie — three weeks old today.

In the smile on John Huseby's face when he speaks about his children.

In Mark Reeves' "Yes" to the call to service.

In the "yes" of missioners around the world.

In the quiet presence of those who so faithfully serve the sick and the poorest of God's poor.

In the courage of so many in New York and Washington and on a plane that was crashed in Pennsylvania. In the heroism of those who responded to horrors or terrorism and continue to respond today.

To hear the Peace of God in the cloistered Maryknoll Sister who recently told me, "Oh Father, there are four of us here in New York, and four in our cloister in Central America, and two in the Sudan, and they're being bombed now."

Or my friends who sponsor other alcoholics and drug addicts in AA and NA and who never give up hope.

To hear the Peace of God in Michael Keister as he works to build a new life for his mother.

Or to see the Peace of God in my brother Michael's Christmas card with the words "Lord, make me an instrument of Your peace."

To see God's promise in the love of Roly and Tamara.

To understand the wonder of God in Warren's orchids or the incredible beauty of tropical fish or the sometimes-mind-numbing chatter of a talking bird. To know that sometimes God is in the Hurricanes when I stand in the Orange Bowl surrounded by friends of many years and listen to the blast of the Sigma

Chi cannon as our team scores again.

To learn from the manatee, the great lumbering sea cows, that God's work is slow but certain and the Kingdom of God will come.

This is my Christmas prayer for you — that you come to see God in all around you and to hear His still small voice in the whispers of your lives and that you know the Promise of the Angels — Peace on Earth and Good Will to all God's People.

2002

If I Tell You,
I'll Have To . . .

It would have been almost all right, if it had just been "one of those weeks." But it had been one of those "last couple of months," and if truth be told, poor Father Danny just hadn't had time to even think about preparing a Christmas homily.

And now, not only was the crunch on but he still didn't have time. So, whether as an expression of his desperation or seeking some ideas or to avoid the whole problem – personally, I think it was the latter – he decided to check-in with the parish philosopher/theologian.

You've got it – Mikey.

Mikey, however, was nowhere to be found – not the school yard (since it was only two days before Christmas, school was out), not the homeless shelter or hanging out at the local *bodega* (corner grocery store). Finally, Dan stopped at Miguelito's home.

"*No esta. Se fue a casa de su abuelita. Esta con catarro y no le permiti salir para jugar con sus amigos* – He's not here," his mother explained. "He went over to his grandmother's because he has a cold and I wouldn't let him go outside and play with his friends."

Two doors down, *Abuelita* – Mikey's grandmother – greeted the priest with an offer of *un cafecito y pastelitos* – Cuban coffee and pastry – and explained that Mikey was out in the big mango tree in the backyard. *"Ese muchachito esta pero loco. No lo entiendo.* That kid is crazy. I just don't understand him. *Ya hace horas que esta en el arbol.* He's been up in that tree for hours now," she said.

And, sure enough, there he was - about twenty maybe twenty-five feet up in one of the biggest mango trees in all of Little Havana.

"Mikey, what are you doin'?"

"Just getting into my role."

"Role? What role?"

"Supposed to be a shepherd in the Christmas play. It's method acting. Saw all about it on the educational or the Arts and Entertainment channel — don't remember which." With each sentence, Mikey moved closer to the ground. "I'm supposed to 'feel' the part. To 'be' the part. I'm a shepherd and the way that I see it is that really good shepherds stayed up in trees. They're supposed to be on the look-out and protect the sheep and you can be a better lookout up high than you can down on the ground. So I'm 'feeling' my part."

Ah, the logic of an eleven-year-old. Who can argue?

"Mikey," the priest began, "I'm stuck. Haven't had a minute to begin to even think about my Christmas sermon. I thought you might have some ideas. What do you think Christmas is all about?"

"Well, Father," Mikey began assuming a strangely dignified, almost aloof attitude, "I know. But, it's a secret and, if I tell you, I'll have to kill you." With that line spoken he convulsed in the laughter of childhood.

When the gales finally gave way, Miguelito climbed back up to the second lowest branch and, almost with the air of a college professor, began his *apologia*. (That's theologian talk for "explanation.")

"We have to understand that it is all a part of the Circle of Life. They talk a lot about that on all the Zoo Life shows that I watch. I have fourteen cassettes of them and whenever I go to see my uncle I always bring all of them with me just because it makes him crazy.

"But really. Think about it. Christmas is about the Circle of Life. Do you see that big huge bush over there. The white one. Abuela calls it the *arbol de Miguel* — "the Michael Tree." When I was just a baby, *Tio* — uncle — gave it to Abuela for Christmas. I was really, really sick and the doctors said that I might not get well and that, if I did, it would take a long, long time. Abuela made Abuelo plant it in front of her kitchen window because she said that every time that she saw it she would pray and tell God to make me all better. She said that she was going to give God one year — until it bloomed again — to make me better and after that God would be in big trouble. Then, right after Christmas, it got very cold and the tree died and Abuela was very disappointed but she kept on praying and telling God what she wanted."

Mikey looked around, almost as if checking for spies

who might hear the next part of his secret and, reassured that there were no listeners except Father Dan, continued (in a whisper), "Abuela doesn't ask God — she tells Him.

"But that spring, the tree came back and look at it now. Every year after Christmas all the leaves fall off and it looks like it dies. Abuelo cuts it way down and then it grows back up again. It is all the Circle of Life. Jesus came at Christmas so that he could die on the Cross and be raised to life in the Resurrection and that is the Circle of Life."

"My God," thought Dan, "What am I doing here — listening to an eight year old tree climbing shepherd-horticulturist-philosopher-theologian?"

But Miguelito was on a roll — one of those "you asked for it and now you're going to get it" kind of the-innocence-of-childhood-put-it-all-on-the-line-and-somehow-make-sense-of-it looks at the mysteries of Faith. "You see, Father, the way I look at it there wasn't much of a beginning or much of an end for Jesus. Born in a pretty dirty stable with a lot of chickens and goats and sheep and dying on a cross with two robbers. That's not very good. But it was the way that he lived that was important. He took care of people and he was kind and he loved and he helped the sick and the poor and that was what was really important and that's why we have the Resurrection.

"Abuela says that God will take care of our beginning and God will take care of our end and that we have to take care of the middle. Sort of like the Michael Tree. God is the one who makes the leaves fall off after it is all done blooming and God is the one who makes the flowers come out at Christmas — but we are the ones who have to take care of it the rest of the year."

"Where's my tape recorder when I really need it," Father Dan cursed himself. "Just put this kid on tape and I've got it made."

"So that's the secret of Christmas?" the priest asked the Cuban kid guru.

"Well, that's a pretty good start. I'll let you figure out the rest on your own," said Miguelito. "Just remember — It's all a part of the Circle of Life. God takes care of the way it begins and the way it ends and we have to take care of the middle. God takes care of us and we have to take care of each other.

"OK, Father? The rest is a secret. You'll have to figure it out for yourself, 'cause, if I tell you, I'll have to kill you."

Super-Duper, Ultra Extra-Strength Christmas

A headache is one thing. A Miguelito headache is something altogether different. And Father Mark was about to be clobbered by an overwhelming need for a couple of truck-sized bottles of Super Duper Ultra-Extra Strength Excedrin.

Depending on your sociological and political perspectives, America is either a "melting pot' or a "mixed salad." Miguelito was, despite his Cuban-, Nica-, Guatemalan-, multi-generational South Florida heritage, the poster child for worldwide Irish immigration. With his brownish-blonde hair, blue eyes, and almost ruddy complexion, there was no doubt that whether from Cuba or Nicaragua or Guatemala or Philadelphia and Old Miami, some of his ancestors traced something back to the Ole Sod. There's just no other way to explain how all those brown eyes and dark hair Latin genes lost their dominance.

And, despite his *appelido* — family name — he had become something of an Irish politician — quick to shake hands, amazing in his ability to remember names, and lightning fast with a laugh that, given his youth, was amazingly hearty and heartfelt. So, it should have come as no surprise that, on the first Sunday of Advent, young Mikey appeared at the door of the Church of Our lady of Perpetual Boredom clipboard and sheaves of paper in hand and collecting signatures on a petition to "the Supreme Pontiff of the Catholic Church in Vatican City, Rome, Italy and the President and Congress of the United States in Washington, District of Columbus, United States of America."

Mikey was calling on the Faithful worldwide to declare the first Tuesday of Advent "the Feast of St. Joseph, the Patron of Happy Surprises."

After so many years, Mark knew instinctively not to engage Mikey head-on; it would be a losing battle and

Mark, a loyal Miami Hurricanes fan, hated to lose. So, he took a more indirect approach: "Mikey, how about meeting me for pastelitos and croquettas this afternoon; you can explain your petition then."

A few hours later, sitting at the window of the *cafeteria* — local coffee shop — Mark marveled at how well Mikey worked the crowd, shaking hands, smiling, *un besito* — a kiss — here, *un abrazo* — a hug — there, "señor" and "señora" everywhere. "Mikey, how do you know everyone?" Mark opened their conversation.

"It's easy, Father," Mikey responded. "Last year you said that part of the miracle of Christmas is that God chooses to live in all his people. So, every day I try to learn someone else's name. When I say hello to them, it's like saying hello to God."

Poor Mark. What's a priest to do when, a year later, an eleven-year-old theologian throws your words back at you.

"I knew it," Mark told himself. "The kid has it all figured out." But now to the business at hand. "Miguelito, tell me about your petition. Joseph, Patron of Happy Surprises? I don't understand. I've never heard of that."

"Tuesday. Every Tuesday *abuela* — grandmother — says that if we pray thirteen Hail Marys in honor of St. Joseph we will receive a pleasant surprise. Sometimes it is *tres leches* for dessert or she'll make *ropa vieja* or *picadillo* or some other dinner that we really like or a movie or just a note in our lunch boxes telling use she loves us. But there's always a pleasant surprise. St. Joseph is the Patron of Pleasant Surprises.

"And, I want to make it a St. Joseph Day because Christmas isn't just about what we're going to get from Santa Claus – that's a secret, not a surprise," said Miguelito, who was personally still hedging his bets on the Santa Claus/Mami and Mapi question. "Abuela says that it's all about how we relate to God. Abuela says believing and trusting are all about surprises. Did Mary and St. Joseph know what was going to happen in their lives? No. It was all a surprise."

Mark wasn't quite sure where the conversation was going. A part of him enjoyed the idea of St. Joseph of Happy Surprises. And, while the pastorally political or politically pastoral part of him was struggling with how to tell Mikey that the petition would go nowhere, the rebel in him decided "What the heck! Oh, to see the expression on the faces of all those guys in cassocks and silk when this hits Rome."

And, despite a natural impatience with just sitting in the cafeteria chowing down on warm *empanadas*, Mark decided to enjoy this time with his Littlest Wiseman. "You know, Mikey, I like your abuela's idea of St. Joseph, Patron of Happy Surprises. Of course, if I say anything about it to the archbishop ..." his voice trailed off into the daydream. "Tell me what else she has to say."

Like an Old Testament prophet delivering the Word of the Lord to his Chosen People, Mikey spoke the *Palabra de Abuela* — The Word of Abuela: "God tells his people 'Be still and know that I am God.' *Lento, lento.* Slow, slow… Stop rushing. Where you are is where God wants you to be. Just be there. Because we're where we're supposed to be, the only thing we have to worry about doing is the right thing. And we already know what that is.

"Abuela says I'm too young to have a girlfriend but she tells me that when I do I should always give orchids not cut flowers. Enjoy orchids. Give them to people you love and as they bloom and each year after they'll serve as a reminder of your love.

"She says, 'Laugh out loud, laugh at yourself — honest, not tiny laughing or worrying about what other people might think, just let go and laugh because Sacred Scripture says ours is a laughing, dancing God.'

"Abuela says that men and women are God's only creatures that can laugh and laugh at themselves and know they are doing it.

"She tells me, 'Pray your emotions. Pray out of your emotions. Make them all a gift to God; they are God's gift to you. Make fun of yourself. It's one of the best ways God gives us to make friends.

"Abuela says that even though I'm still small I should 'Carry small children on your head and on your shoulders. Let them see the beauty of God's world. If it was good enough for the Child Jesus, it's certainly good enough for them. And forget safety. Just have some fun. Cry freely. Not just in pain and sorrow, cry in happiness and joy and because you're alive and because you feel and because sometimes it just feels good – no it feels great – to feel."

Mikey continued, "Abuela says God gave us ears to listen and tongues to hold." At this Mikey leaned forward and, with absolute seriousness, reported, "I understand the ears bit but no matter how hard I try I can't hold onto my tongue.

"Abuela says that Christmas comes at the end of the year to remind us of how we are supposed to live today and all of the year to come. That we should be good news to someone every day.

"Abuela says, 'Be a surprise. Do something nice and unexpected for someone every day. But make sure no one knows about it. Talk to animals – not just your dog or cat. Talk to humming birds, to squirrels, to turtles, and to the big lumbering raccoons and opossums.

[I'll bet this is the first time in years that any priest has ever said the word "opossums" during a Christmas Eve homily.]

"Sit in your car and enjoy the complete story on National Public Radio. Just let go and feel your emotions – pride and hope, sorrow and empathy, challenge and victory, loss and confidence and fear, love and promise.' Abuela says that God the Father felt all of these at the instant of the birth of Jesus.

Miguelito continued his abuela-quoting monologue, "Pray for others. Quietly, secretly. Pray for the person whom you don't know but you do know that you should be praying for. And know that every now and then God will tell you when to tell someone that you've been praying for them."

"Abuela says to be grateful for the gift of life. She says it was the very, very first gift of Christmas. Abuela says that we have to take care of our brains — challenge them and keep them sharp because they are that special gift from God that makes us different from all the rest of Creation. She says that we have to take care of our bodies because that is where God lives with us and in the World."

Two Cuban coffees and enough croquetas to stop the heart of a charging rhino later, Mark knew he had to call it quits — no one's heart can take two Cuban coffees and that many croquettas in just an hour and keep functioning. Besides, he had to make plans for the Masses of the First Week of Advent, including Tuesday, Feast of St. Joseph Guardian of the Holy Family, Hero of Christmas and Patron of Happy Surprises.

2006

Eyes of Compassion and Hands of Service

A few days ago, I found a great quote from St. Teresa of Avila. It seemed especially appropriate as I reflected upon the Mystery of Christmas: "Christ has no body but yours, no hands, no feet on earth but yours; yours are the eyes with which he looks compassion on this world."

Last June, when Gene and Ryan visited me in China, we went to Mass at the Cathedral in Xi'an, together with two of my favorite students and translators — Sico and David, neither of whom had ever been in a church before. Only after Mass did Ryan tell me how carefully Sico, one of the leaders of his campus Communist youth group, and David – observed and followed my every move – standing, sitting, kneeling when I did; folding their hands as I did; even extending them at the words of consecration as I concelebrated from afar with the priest at the altar; and, finally, despite the fact that I told them that I would be right back when I went to Communion, following immediately behind me to receive the Body of Christ. David later explained that he had grown up in a Buddhist home and they always eat when they are finished praying; Sico reported that he was imitating his "honored teacher."

Looking forward to tonight, I wondered how I might explain the mysteries of Christmas to my friends.

Father Mark had a problem. Of course, there was the perpetual problem of the archbishop and all those folks at the archbishop's office, but he had managed to get around them by taking a couple of years in a special teaching position at a school in China. He even managed to land a spot in a Chinese law school where he taught American contract law.

He was back now – helping out in a parish in Little

Havana. And Father Mark had a problem. He was an occasional gambler — and, to make matters worse, he was a secret gambler, hooked on the Lottery. Oh, he had his justifications. It was, he told himself, the cheapest thrill you can get for five bucks a week in Florida. But, unlike other lottery junkies, Father Mark had developed a theological justification for his gambling: "You can't win if you don't play and God knows I deserve to win." So, he bet a combination of numbers — his age and birthday, ordination date, his nephew's birthday, the year he was born.

More importantly, after China, he had figured out precisely what he'd do should he ever manage to win big. And, it seems that God had a pretty good idea — not quite perfect, but pretty good, because one Saturday not too long after returning to the States and when the estimated payout was right around $43 million, Mark hit on five out of six — birthdays, ordination dates, his nephew's age. Not once, but twice on the same card.

He put aside money to make certain that teachers in the parish school would get some much-deserved bonuses; established a few "Secret Santa" accounts for parishioners of all ages, and then he splurged. Seems that, while in China, Father Mark had developed some really special relationships with a few of his students and, each week, part of his "cheapest thrill you can get for five bucks in Florida" had been the dream of bringing

Sico, David, and Thompson to Miami for an American holiday.

It took some doing — nothing like a well-positioned friend or two and a little Catholic guilt on some folks in Washington and the embassy in Beijing to grease the wheels of international diplomacy. The guys, all medical school students in their early mid-twenties, arrived not long after Thanksgiving. The first two weeks or so went well — Disney World and the Kennedy Space Center, overnight in the Keys, a daytrip to the Everglades. But Christmas was fast approaching, and with command performances at the archbishop's office, teaching, and parish demands, Mark's time was no longer his own.

So, on the Sunday before Christmas he sent out an S.O.S. from the pulpit and into the breach — shining 12-speed bike and all — rode the infamous Miguelito. In fact, he didn't really "ride" — at least not in the classic sense of riding. It was more like fumbled, bumbled, slipped and slid and dragging three extra bikes that Mikey made his appearance. In typical Mikey fashion, out spilled an explanation that would have required an FBI comput-er to decipher: *Tio* — Uncle — Jose works in a bike store, borrow, round town, show your friends, explain, help to understand, *Noche Buena* — Christmas Eve, — *lechon* — roast pork, — something about "Chinese like pork," and a "don't worry, Father."

Mikey had it all planned: He had seen a History

Channel special about China and how everyone rode bicycles (Mark didn't quite have the heart to tell him that private cars had started to outnumber bicycles in parts of the Middle Kingdom) and Mikey figured that he would show Father Mark's Chinese guests Miami the way that only a twelve-year-old can. He knew that buses and Metro Rail provide special space for bicycles and had outlined routes and bike paths that could get them any and everywhere.

So began one of the most unique weeks of tourism imaginable. All the more remarkable because, even back home, with his Chinese friends Mark continued the practice he maintained in China of carefully avoiding any discussion of religion and Faith. He knew his friends were typically Chinese — the grandchildren of Buddhists, one a campus leader of the Communist party, all men-of-no-faith.

Mikey felt no such inhibition. In fact, for Miguelito there was no subject that was too personal or too out of bounds.

The week before Christmas he became the bicycling, tour-guiding, Spanish- and English-speaking, all-round expert on all-things Christmas — American and Cuban-American — and all things theological.

"We have Christmas in China, now," Thompson explained, "but it is all about gifts and shopping malls and more and more Santa Clauses and many people are beginning to become upset that we're losing our Chinese and our Buddhist and our Taoist values to Western culture. We don't understand Christian Christmas"

"Hey," answered Miquelito, "In some ways it's not so very different here. But, for people of Faith, Christmas is not about what we give and get from others. It's about what God has given to us.

"But, I don't understand the statues — the woman, the shepherds, the men with the crowns," David added.

As they peddled around town, Miquelito was about to enter his theological element but said, "Let's ride around for a while. Maybe I can help you understand." And so the Four Wise Men rode.

It wasn't terribly far to Miami Children's Hospital and so, one morning Tia Ana, who worked there, gave the young Chinese doctors the royal tour. David almost ended up in the emergency room himself — he thought his heart would stop when he saw Miami Heat players distributing Christmas gifts. The next day they headed east to a house near Jackson Memorial Hospital where the Sisters from the Missionaries of Charity feed hundreds of homeless. The guys thought it was great that they could hoist their bikes onto a bus for a ride across town but the idea of spending part of their holiday peeling potatoes to make dinner for homeless people was a whole new concept.

There were *pastelitos* — *Cuban pastries* — and *cafecitos*

— Cuban coffee. After a stop at Café Americana, Thompson added "catch a buzz" to his American English vocabulary. There were the Seaquarium and Viscaya, The Grove and South Beach during the day. There was *ropa vieja* and *moros* — shredded pork with black beans and rice. None of the boys had ever seen the ocean or even a really big lake before and Miguel had to call Tío Paul with his pick-up truck for a ride home one night when it was impossible to get Sico out of the water.

On Wednesday morning, Mikey invited his Wise Men to join him bell-ringing for Camillus House for the homeless at Dadeland. And Thursday was an all-day adventure with Habitat for Humanity — finishing off two houses to make sure their families would have "Homes for the Holidays."

"We don't understand volunteering the way you do it in America," explained David.

"It's the Christian response," answered Mikey. "Not because it's Christmas — even though we only bell-ring at Christmas — but because Jesus taught that we must feed the hungry, clothe the naked, visit the sick and the imprisoned, and shelter the homeless. It is what Christmas is all about.

"But sometimes we forget that these are the things that make us Christian," he continued. "Sometimes we get so caught up in worrying about politics and illegal immigrants that we forget that Joseph and Mary were strangers in a foreign land. That there was nowhere for them because Mary was going to have a baby and hotels didn't want to have them — something about law and keeping things clean. And no one had the courage to give Mary and Joseph a place to stay. I don't understand all of that but I know that Jesus gave us a new law — to love one another. And, we need Christmas to remind us."

"But the statues," asked David later in the day. "You never explained the statues."

"Oh, they remind us, too," explained Miguel as they downed hotdogs, chips and sodas at Matheson Hammock — Sico and David wanted to be as close to the ocean as possible and as often as possible.

"Oh, we call it the stable or the manger; if you're really smart or want to pretend you are, you call it the *crèche* but it reminds us of the very first and most important part of the Christmas story — that God came as a stranger, that he was so rejected that, even before he was born, there was no place for him in the hearts of so many people that it is easier to focus on Santa Claus and shopping malls than on the message of Peace on Earth and Good Will toward all people.

"Mary reminds us of both the greatness and the goodness of God. That God is a source of joy and all things are possible in and through him. All God asks of us is all he asked of Mary — to love gently as she gently loved her son. And Joseph — he's just a good man, doing what is right because his heart tells him it is right. He reminds us that in the simplicity of honest, gentle service we all bring Jesus into the hearts and lives of others.

"The shepherds were the poorest people in Israel; they were the people no one wanted, but when the Savior of the World was born, they were the first with whom the Good News was shared. They remind us that the poor are always with us and we must see them as the special place in which we find God."

"The guys with the crown. I don't understand them," said Thompson, who prided himself on speaking the best English and knowing the most American slang; he said "guys" a lot. "If the shepherds are the poor, why the guys with the crowns?"

"Ah," explained Miguel, "That's the part where you come in. We call them the Three Wise Men or the Three Kings. The shepherds remind us that Jesus came to share Good News with the Jewish People. In Tradition the Wise Men are Black, Brown, and Yellow. In Tradition they come from the East — like Sico, David and Thompson. They come to the stable because they are looking, exploring, searching for something bigger, greater, more eternal than they are. Their statues are here to remind us that Jesus is Good News not just for the Jewish People but for everyone."

"And the Angel," queried Sico, the most philosophical of the Wise Men.

"In many ways," said Mikey, "the angel had the most important role of all. He announces to the shepherds, the Wise Men and all who would hear that Jesus had come as Prince of Peace, Christ the Lord. He reminds us that all of us are called to be Peace Makers, to do Justice."

Day by day, the Four Wise Men toured Miami, dropping off food to *unos ancianos* – some elderly folks, collecting bags of gifts from neighborhood shops and delivering them to fire stations and the Marines for Toys For Tots. As Christmas Eve approached, Sico had one more question: "But why do you go to church for Christmas? Our parents and grandparents did not go to the Buddhist temples in big groups the way you Christians go to church"

"Because," explained Theologian Mikey, "Jesus calls us to be a people – a community. Because being kind, being honest, being hopeful, being peace makers, being like Jesus isn't always easy. We are our best when we are with and supported by others. We are our best when we are reminded and remind each other that the mystery of Jesus, the mystery of what we believe in, is not all about me, or you, or you or you. It is about Us – you and you and you – the Three Wise Men from the East and Father Mark and my parents and los abuelos, all together. When we remember that it is about Peace to All People on Earth."

Somewhere around four-thirty on Christmas Eve afternoon, Mark saw a blur as the Four Biking Wise Men raced past the front of the church. Then came the sound of screeching bike wheels, quick u-turns, and Mikey and Company explaining. "We're going to get ready for *Noche Buena*. Abuela says dinner will begin at eight."

"*A la hora China-Americana*, — at Chinese-American time," said David, proud of his developing Chin-Spanglish."

"Abuela wants the whole family to be ready for *la misa*," explained Miquel.

"Enjoy the lechon," Father Mark told his friends. "When you go home, you'll be able to tell your families all about how Miguel's *familia* celebrates this holiday. But after dinner, why don't you three just get a good night's sleep. You don't have to worry about coming to church." Mark was still concerned about avoiding any possible pressure on his guests and being Chinese-politically correct.

"Oh, no," said David, quickly assuming the role of group spokesman. "We will be there."

So it was that, as Mark began the Christmas Eve Mass, he spied the Four Wise Men — Miquelito and the Three Visitors From the East. As Mikey signed himself with the Sign of the Cross, so did they; when Mikey stood, sat or knelt, so did they; when he folded his hands in prayer, the Wise Men folded theirs in quiet wonder and contemplation. And, …. (Shooosh… Don't tell! Father Mark might get in even more trouble…) As Mikey joined the procession of his family to the altar for Communion, so did Three Wise Men From the East looking, exploring, searching for something bigger, greater, more eternal, hope-filled and holier.

In that moment Father Mark recognized that not only did God know that he deserved to win the Lottery but somehow this Procession of the Wise Men from the East just might have been a part of that wondrous plan of the Divine. It is, indeed, Mark determined, as St. Teresa of Avila has written, "Christ has no body but yours, no hands, no feet on earth but yours; yours are the eyes with which he looks compassion on this world."

About Wingless Angels

It was a marvel-to-behold. During the family's *Noche Buena* — Christmas Eve — meal, Miguelito consumed not one but two full plates — everything: rice and black beans, *yucca, plantanos maduros, lechon* — fried sweet bananas, roast pork — and turkey. Family and guests alike wondered wide-eyed and open-mouthed "Where did he, where can he put it all?" but a laughing Mikey simply answered, "I'm a growing boy and I'm in training."

A response which drew proud smiles from *los abuelos* — the grandparents — and a quiet acceptance from just about everyone else.

Now, however, it was time for the *Misa del Gallo* — Midnight Mass — to begin and Mikey was curled up on the church pew, fast asleep against his father's left shoulder, feet resting on his mother's lap; and, as if his sleeping wasn't embarrassment enough to his mother who insisted that "Tradition is tradition and in my family we always go to Misa del Gallo," the little devil was snoring.

Although you wouldn't know it just at this moment, Miguelito had become quite the theologian. That is, if a nine-year-old fourth-grader can really be a theologian. For Miguelito, it had been an angelic year. This is not to say that he had been an angel; rather, it had been a year of angels — on the cover of magazines, in stores, statues on selves in his grandmother's home, pictures of angels and books about angels. And Mikey had spent a lot of time thinking about angels. So, if angels are somehow connected with God and if theology is thinking about God and the things of God, then Mikey had become a theologian.

His curiosity had come gradually. Somewhat like the changes in the way that his mother spoke to him. For quite a while she had called him "Pumpkin," then "Angel" and, of late, "You Little Devil." He understood, of course, that angels really don't come from pumpkins, but it was "the little devils from angels" transition that really had him wondering.

In school people had spent weeks preparing for Christmas and last night's Christmas pageant. As a result, his theological inquiries knew no bounds. He had — with great facility — quickly memorized and could deliver with a forced-from-the-bottom-of-his-chest basso profondo voice his one and only line (his ticket to stardom and fame): "There is no room in the inn."

The essentials of great acting having been clearly mastered, he set himself to the theological task at hand — the contemplation of angels. And most certainly his position — off stage and surrounded by squirming kindergarteners and first and second graders getting ready for a Christmas pageant — provided the perfect setting.

First, there was the issue of angels' wings. A family friend who often brought flowers and orchids to Mikey's mother, the old *"Rustico"* — the "rustic one," as his uncle called him — had once told Mikey that the multicolored petals of orchids were feathers fallen from angels' wings. It was, Mikey thought, a great story. But he had never seen a picture of an angel with colored wings, and, even when, on special occasions, his family's African-American friend dressed him up "all nice and special" and took him to her church, the angels were the same — with Black faces, of course, but all with white wings. Though he enjoyed the Rustico's story, he didn't *really* believe it. Moreover, he had determined, if angels are about serving God and His people and God and His people are everywhere, they really didn't need to fly to get to where they belonged and were already there. So it was that Miguel categorically negated the very idea of angel wings.

At the same time that Miguelito was abolishing the idea of angels' wings, he discovered one idea that he thought he would definitely keep: Guardian Angels. These were, he decided, one of God's better inventions — if angels are invented at all.

Guardian Angels are supposed to protect us, keep up from harm. And God knows that nine-year-old, fourth-grade boys have a knack for getting into harm's way. Yes, Mikey decided to keep Guardian Angels and, surprisingly, one day announced to his totally astonished parents that he, Miguel, had not one — the way most people do — but *two Guardian Angels*. One was for his American side; he spoke English and ate hamburgers. But the other was Cuban; he spoke Spanish and ate black beans and rice and *ropa vieja* — shredded beef.

Beyond this, however, if truth be told, the more he thought the more confused he became. And adults weren't much help at all in figuring out this angel question. They seemed to see angels everywhere and a lot of people seemed — if you listened to adults — to be angels. Why only last week Miguel and his mother had taken Christmas gifts to a school out in Immokalee. It was run, his mother said, for the Indian kids from Central America by a nun, which in itself struck Mikey as quite strange because this lady was really... Well, she was really big, and if she was "none" he couldn't figure out what she was "none" of because as far as he could see there was too much of her to be "none." But, as they drove away, his mother discussed with him all that the lady did to help the "Indian kids" and then she added, "She's a real angel." That, thought Mikey, is a most unusual idea — a big lady angel who speaks Spanish and English.

Then there was the time that his grandmother was talking about a doctor and a nurse who had taken care of his grandfather when he was in the hospital. "*Angeles son, de verdad* — they are truly angels," declared Abuela.

Or his uncle who was speaking about the *anciana* — a really old — lady with pure white hair and a spring in her step, who caused Miguelito to have to run to keep up with her. "You're such an angel," *Tio* — uncle — once told her. "A devil of an angel, but an angel," he said. To which the old lady anciana replied, "*Portate bien, mijito, y si no puedas, gozalo* — Be good young man, and if you can't, enjoy it." Now Mikey didn't quite understand all that, and, from the way the adults laughed, he wasn't quite sure whether it was the devil or the angel speaking.

There were other angels. El Rustico and his wife who kept abuela's home so full of orchids; a lady at the neighborhood *bodega* — corner market — who seemed never to be without a smile and always a piece of candy for any kid who came through her checkout line; the young doctor's wife whom he met at his first football game and who had a new baby, or the strange "Sister" with whom Abuelo worked once a week feeding homeless men.

So it was that Miguelito revised four thousand years of the theology of angels and determined that, generally speaking, angels don't have wings; if you have parents from another country, you'd better double check because you just might have two different Guardian Angels; angels come in all shapes and sizes, and most of them live right around us. All we have to do is open our eyes and they are here for us to see.

It was this Miguelito, the Theologian, who slept through most of the *Misa del Gallo* — Midnight Mass — until communion time. As the priest and Eucharistic ministers moved toward their stations to distribute communion, Mikey roused himself, tucked his shirt back into his pants, straightened his red tie and jacket and declared to his wondering parents "Let's go."

"Where," they asked almost with one voice.

"To communion," he answered with an almost "of course" tone to his voice. "I'm in training. A growing angel. We all go to Communion. We need to go to communion, if we're going to be angels."

It's probable that no one else in the church that night heard Mikey's response. And, if they had, some might argue with his theology, but this night we celebrate the birth of a child who comes precisely that we might all go to Communion — that in our humanity we might enjoy a special union with our God, the Word Made Flesh Who Dwells Amongst Us.

This night we celebrate the birth of the World Made Flesh Who Dwells Amongst Us — in others, in ourselves, in Communion — the Word Made Flesh Who Dwells Amongst Us and calls us, each by name, so that, as His brothers and sisters we might be a little more like angels.

2004

$\mathcal{L}$eft Behind, Little Sun

In China today, between a hundred million and two hundred million people are referred to as illegal "internal migrants."

They leave their homes and families, and most tragically, their children, in the countryside to travel to cities where, too often, they live almost as homeless, working in construction and factory jobs so that they can provide for those they leave behind. It's the only way they can afford the costs of medical care and tuition for their children.

In Chinese, the children left behind in the countryside are referred to as *liu shou* or "left behind" and it is said of their parents, caught in poverty and migration, that "they are eating bitterness." A child whose parents are able to care well for him or her is called *"xiao taiyang"* or "little sun."

Many years ago, Michael Keister introduced me to Leonard Traficanti and some years later, Michael as the best man, and I celebrated the ceremony in which Leonard married Christine.

Recently, Leonard and Christine went to China and returned with their own *xiao taiyang*. They were supposed to be here this evening, but got caught by the snow in Cincinnati. This is, in part, for them. As this is published, Leonard and Christine now have two adopted daughters – Vivian Xiao Nan and Olivia Lu Yin. Two "little suns."

Mark's brain was in full melt-down mode and his body wasn't far behind. If someone could invade his spiritual self, it might appear that he was praying but, in fact, he was begging and negotiating: "Just five minutes, God. Just five or ten minutes to close my eyes and sit here and rest. Just fifteen minutes, God, that's all I need."

It was only three o'clock in the afternoon and he was so tired that his body was convinced that it was well after midnight and his mind was silently cursing that it wasn't. He was in the midst of one of those infamous Isabel Singletary moments – you know when it's December 23rd and you still think that Christmas is next week.

He thought he was going to sit down but instead he fell – hard – like a bag of rocks onto the too hard seat of the pew. The sound of his own thudding body shook him almost as badly as the cataclysmic vibrations that moved up his spinal cord and from rear-end to knees and on down to his ankles.

But Mark wasn't the only one startled by his unmodulated collapse. He had thought he would enjoy a few minutes of silence, alone in the cavernous church. In fact, he had been so blind-tired when he thudded that he didn't see the leg casually thrown over the pew in front of him or the foot that he almost sat on or the figure sprawled out along the pew next to him.

I can't tell you who was more startled, exhausted Mark or the jumping-to-his-feet teen.

"Wow, Padre, careful there," the gangling figure – all arms and legs and tussled hair – was saying, even as Mark simultaneously cursed the loss of the quiet time for which he had not yet finished begging and experienced a blast of adrenaline that would now make quiet impossible. For a few seconds, Mark watched as the arms and legs whirled this way and that, eventually planting feet on the ground and then settling awkwardly back into the pew next to him.

"Padre, you almost sat on me. And my mother says that *I* don't look where I'm going!'"

"Mikey, what are you doing here," Father Mark asked in a tone that was somewhere between an honest question and a desperate "Oh, God, can't I ever get a break?"

"Just thinking, Father" came a voice no longer that of a child but still a long way from that of a man.

"Thinking?" Mark echoed, despite a fear that the answer would open untold worlds. At the same time, he had an unhappy sense that God had heard his pleas – five minutes, ten minutes, fifteen minutes – and was saying, "Nahhhhhh."

"I should have stopped at the ten minutes; I might have gotten away with that," he told himself. "Thinking? About?"

"About carcinogenic aromatic polymorphous hydrocarbons and my new girlfriend."

"Carcinogenic...?"

"Carcinogenic aromatic polymorphous hydrocarbons. I was listening to National Public Radio last week, and Father, did you know that there are more carcinogenic aromatic polymorphous hydrocarbons in Catholic churches than anywhere else in the world."

"Two roads diverged in the woods," thought Mark, "and I chose carcinogenic aromatic... whatever the H."

"And, Father, just think about it. So far this week..."

Mark's mind was reeling, "I don't want to think about it; I can't even say it."

But Miguelito was on a Miguelito-roll, "So far this week we've had four funerals and with all the incense you keep throwing around and all the candles in front of the Blessed Mother and St. Joseph and *la Caridad* – Our Lady of Charity, Patroness of Cuba – the air is full of carcinogenic aromatic polymorphous hydrocarbons and my new girlfriend is coming to Mass on Friday night and I don't want them to hurt her."

"Ah," the light was beginning to brighten in Mark's

exhaustion-dimmed brain. The smoke of incense and candle wax. "Change the subject," he told himself. "Mikey, you have a new girlfriend...."

"Oh, Father, she's beautiful." His eyes began to glass over and it seemed as though he would wax poetic. "Her eyes are so brown, like a little Cubanita but, *Abuela* says that they are almond-shaped. *Tio* — Uncle — Leo (his name is Leonardo but I call him Tio Leo), the Lion Uncle, and *Tia* — Aunt — Christina went to China to adopt her. *Es una Chinita Cubanita Americanita*. Her parents, maybe just her mother, couldn't keep her. She would have grown up a *liu shou* — left behind. I think that when her mother gave her up she must have eaten much bitterness. But now she's *xiao tai yang* — *ella es un pequena sol* — a little sun. And she's smart and she smiles when I say "*ni hao*" — that's 'hello' in Chinese and we all love her so much and I say she's my new girlfriend, even though she's just a baby."

Mikey was thoroughly smitten. "And, I've just been sitting here — okay, lying here — and thinking about Olivia and how cool it is that she is part of our family and about the Christmas crib and..."

There was no stopping him now. He had climbed over the pew and was walking up and down the aisle, singing the praises of his new girlfriend. Now he was in the sanctuary, sitting among the statues that had been placed around the Christmas crib.

"Father, did you ever really think about all the different people who were part of the Christmas crib? Look. How many Wise Men are there?"

Ah, now they were on his terms. "Three," said Mark, and, because his competitive spirit was kicking into full gear, he added "Caspar, Melchior and Balthasar."

"Naaaaaaaaah, Father. That's tradition; the Scriptures don't say how many and they don't name them. I think there should be four. So, I found an old one in the sacristy closet from when I was a kid and stuck it in the manger scene. So far, no one has even noticed that there's four and besides, they're not supposed to be out until January 6. "

Mark just knew he was being drawn into another Miguelito vortex. "Four?"

"Think about it, Padre. Each figure in the crib tells us something about Faith and Life.

"This Wise Man is Gratitude. He understands that everything in life is just as it should be — that the Gift of Life is enough all by itself. He understands that everything — good, bad, happy, painful, long lasting and temporary, successes and failures, addictions and recoveries and relapses — are all gifts we have been given without ever having to ask for them. His gold is a simple prayer: 'Thank you, O Lord, for sunrises and sunsets, for children's laughter and parents' hopes, for the kiss of a loved one, and the promises of tomorrow.'

"In front of him is Wise Man Humility. He understands that all those things for which he is grateful are his because God chose to freely gift him. He understands that, for no merit of his own, totally apart from anything that he has done or can do, God has singled him out to be the special recipient of his unique gifts. He knows that God has created him in God's own image, that he is imperfect and incomplete and that, no matter how hard he tries or gives up, his heart can only be at peace when in and with God. That's Humility. He's got a great prayer: 'Lord, God of Perfection, I offer my imperfections and incompleteness to you, like the evening sacrifice of Incense.'

"Then there's Wise Man Tolerance. Tolerance is cool because he always makes sure that there are a couple of rips and tears in his royal cloaks, even if he's the only one who knows they're there. It is his way of reminding himself that he's not perfect and he's not alone in his imperfections, that each and every one of us is still being brought to perfection by the hand of God. And so, he has learned to tolerate the imperfections of others because they are just expressions or reflections of his own imperfections. Father, did you know that myrrh is scented oil? Tolerance prays: 'Pour over us, O Lord of Kindness, the rich oil of acceptance – of ourselves and all others.'

"And, finally, the Fourth Wise Man – Forgiveness. He believes that the Kingdom of God is always Coming

— that it is coming to perfection in himself and others. And so, he's willing to let go of the past and feelings that he did not get something that he wanted or deserved or desired. He has learned that, because God continues to give him precisely what he needs, he does not have to constantly try to get more than what he has. He can give up desperation and begin to live in the moment — the now. He understands that life won't — can't — give him everything but what it has given him is more than enough. And so, he celebrates each unique moment — especially this moment. He doesn't long for the palace and the company of the rich and powerful but is content among shepherds, in the poverty of a stable, empty-handed, kneeling before an infant."

Mark watched in awe as Miguelito crawled among the states of the Christmas stable.

"Now the Shepherds. They're just the greatest. They know precisely who they are — they're shepherds. They watch the seasons come and go; they see the work of God in all around them. They trust, they hope, they believe that God is good. Did you ever notice the shepherds in manger scenes, Padre? Some stand, some lay down among the sheep. But each of them is grounded. They know just who they are — shepherds — folks that God calls His own.

"Mary," Miguelito said and stood, stepped back, turned toward the priest, turned back to the manger scene and began anew.

"Did ya' ever notice, Padre, that we say they're the three Kings. But, there's no servants. Have you ever seen a king without servants? Did ya' ever wonder why there's no servants at the manger? I kind of think it's because she is *the* Servant. 'Behold the Servant of the Lord,' she says. Some say that St. Francis said 'Preach the Gospel always, with words when necessary.' She preaches the Gospel with silent service. Isn't that the lesson for all of us?"

Mark was desperately wondering whether his brain could capture – and retain – all this. Miguelito was, after all, writing his Christmas sermon for him. "Mikey," he started to interrupted because he really wanted to take some notes, "Do you mind if ..." But Miguelito was racing to his close.

"Now, Joseph," said Mikey. "Everyone says that Jesus is the reason for the season but the truth is it's Joseph. Without him, there'd be no Christmas. He's the hero. Like Tio Leo, he adopts Jesus as his own. Shelters, provides for him, protects him, cares for Mary. Of all the folks in the manger, it is Joseph who best reflects God. The same way that Joseph adopted Jesus and called Him his own, at Christmas and through Jesus, God adopts us and calls us His own."

With his last and final insight, Mikey straightened himself, moved away from the manger, and resumed his sprawl in the pew next to Mark.

"So, Father, that's what I was thinking about when you almost broke my leg. Thinking about Olivia — my Chinese-Cuban-American girlfriend, how wonderful that Uncle Leonard and Aunt Christine adopted her the way that Joseph adopted Jesus and now they are going to adopt another baby, another "Little Sun," the way Joseph did. And I was thinking about how all the different figures in the manger teach us something about who we are and how to live."

"Mikey," Mark began in the depth of his exhaustion, "You've practically written my sermon for me. Do you mind if I…"

"Sure, Father, use anything you want. But just remember my new girlfriend is going to be at Mass on Christmas Eve. Maybe you could cut down on some of the carcinogenic aromatic polymorphous hydrocarbons. Easy on the incense. Maybe use a little more holy water.

"See you for Noche Buena, Father. And, you'll get to meet my new girlfriend."

2012

The Christmas Mitzvah

Over the years, I have reminded people that the Gospel — the great and eternal Good News — was a story. With a Prologue and Opening Chapter, a Climax and Epilogue. Tonight, we celebrate the Prologue, "Peace be with you," and we celebrate Joy — the great climax of the Resurrection that is made possible by this Prologue of God choosing to live amongst His People.

I love to challenge Christians by asking them to recall the Great Commandment of Jesus. Eventually, they'll remember "This is my commandment: That you love one another." But, if you want to have some fun, dare them to come up with the Reason for the Great Commandment. Bet them a drink, a six-pack, a China or Rome vacation, or just a couple of bucks. They'll never get it: "This is my commandment: That you love one another, so that my joy may be in you and your joy may be complete."

Tonight, we celebrate the Gift of His Peace and the Promise of His Joy.

◄◦►◄◦►◄◦►◄◦►◄◦►◄◦►◄◦►◄◦►◄◦►◄◦►◄◦►

I love the phrase "to be smitten" − to fall inexplicably, unexpectedly, in love with someone. That "lub-dub" feeling.

From the beginning, the "smittening" was mutual. But, let's back up just a moment because there were the four smittens and four who were smitteners and we really ought to know their backgrounds.

Although it had been planned long before she was born that she would be known as Katerina, from his very first glimpse, her father called her his "Joy." But her mother insisted that Katerina Alegria Valdes was *"como demasiado"* − a "little too much." So it was that this raven-haired, huge brown-eyes, dimple-cheeked, absolute cutie, who could melt a man's heart with the gift of the slightest smile, was known as Katerina Joy Valdes.

Then there was the Gang of Three — Gerald, Daniel and Michael, the third better known as Miguelito to some and Mikey to many. Best buddies since… well, simply best friends for as long as anyone could remember.

Especially during the summer, the Bicycle Boys explored every nook and neighborhood between Domino Park and the Palmetto from Calle Ocho to the university campus. It was often — erroneously — alleged that Mikey was the leader; in truth, more often than not, he was simply the first to decide on a new direction or a new adventure and Dan and Gerald — Geraldito — just rode hard to catch-up and team-up.

Then, one especially sultry July afternoon — and, wonder of wonder, only a block from Dan's home — the three were smitten. It was instantaneous. They were riding to it-really-doesn't-matter-where when they passed an unremarkable — except for a huge mango tree and a giant plastic wading pool in the front yard — home. And, right in the middle of that pool, a seemingly crying-for-no-reason, and maybe a year or two younger than the boys, Katerina Joy Valdes. The boys stopped, approached rather gingerly, asked all the right probing questions, and searched for an appropriate adult. When they were completely frustrated by their inability to quiet this charming beauty, they did what any self-respecting member of the Bicycle Gang would do: they backed off about fifteen or twenty feet and then ran and threw themselves into the pool, clothes and all. Jumping, splashing, laughing, just plain being The Bicycle Gang on another adventure. And, wonder of wonders, Katerina Joy laughed and splashed and joined in the play as though the tears of seconds earlier never were.

From that moment and for the next few years, they were all smitten. Joy (Katerina was just *too... you know,* for these rough-and-tumblers) had three new boyfriends – and older men, at that. And the boys... they were big brothers, guardian protectors, knights on shiny bikes who, whenever possible, included her in everything. She often rode on their adventures; they were in and out of each other's homes as though they were their own; they shared meals at their families' tables and learned each other's traditions and foods. Nicaraguan red beans and rice, *indio viejo* and *vigoron* at Geraldito's; Cuban black bean soup, *bolice* and *picadillo* at Mikey's and Joy's; and, on Fridays, Shabbat roast chicken at Dan's. And it was here that Daniel's paternal *media mashugana abuelita* – little mashugana grandmother – introduced them to bagels and latkes and blintzes. (Now, don't try to figure out how Danielito has a media-mashugana abuelita; this is my story and I get to do anything I want in it.) Thus, it was, at Daniel's home for Friday Shabbat dinner, they heard what would become the Princess's favorite word: *Mitzvah — a simple, quiet act of kindness, a minor miracle in which God chooses to be secret.*

At the Princess's insistence, mitzvah — actually, it's mitzvot in the plural – became an important part of their adventures. They discovered that, if they could dumpster-dive on just the right day of the week at two flower shops on Red Road, they'd find sunflowers and roses and Gerber daisies that made great surprise leave-them-on-Mrs.-Garcia's-door-step-and-run-and-ride-away bouquets; they learned that if they promised to police the parking lot of Cafeteria Habana the owner would give them all the left over — and still really good — corquetas and empanadas on Tuesday and Friday and they could take them to la familia Rodriguez to help fill an almost empty refrigerator. They found that they could make *los viejos* — the old people — of the nursing home on the Twelfth Street smile if they just stopped and sang some old songs and said hello or played checkers or dominos. They opened doors and carried packages, picked up and threw away trash, and even interrupted an adventure to help an old fisherman carry his poles back to his car. They learned *mitzvah — a simple, quiet act of kindness, a little miracle in which God chooses to be secret.*

Now don't get me wrong. This was not an altogether perfect smittenship. Joy could be… how do I explain this? With a smile, with those dimples and cocker-span-iel-big-brown eyes, she could set their hearts afire. And, if she disapproved, she could wither the three with a heart-rending look.

And, no one, believe me, no one was more demand-ing of perfection when the three were assigned as altar boys — yes, even Dan, because not even the priest could break up this winning team — for weddings or funer-als or special occasions like Holy Week and Easter and Christmas Eve. She'd inspect their robes and how the cords around their waists were tied, critique how high or low they held the cross or candles, and God-forbid one begin to nod off — no matter how long or quietly Father Mark preached.

Now there's something important to remember about kids this age. My father used to say things "go in one ear and out the other." Ooooh, he was so wrong! Say something, especially if you don't think they're around or might hear, and it goes in one ear, raddles around for a while in that seemingly empty head, finds a few special neurons where it imprints to be repeated when you're least expecting it, and only then does it go out the other ear.

And although he didn't know it, that's what hap-pened at Easter. Father Mark gave, he believed, a better than average homily: Easter, not Christmas, is the most important event of the Church's life, and all of nature attests to the Resurrection. He even used the example of the caterpillar — the person — ultimately spun into the cocoon of death and wondrously conquering death in the slender of the butterfly, the first symbol of the Resurrection in Christian art.

It was an extremely long and late Easter service. But, despite the nodding-headed Bicycle Gang of Three altar boys, his words did go in one small ear, rattled around for a while until they found just the right neurons, made a long-lasting contact, and went out the other.

So it was that on the morning of Christmas Eve, the Gang of Three and their princess side-kick, were asked to do the heavy lifting and moving when the *viejas* — the little old lady volunteers — prepared the altar's Christmas crib. They unwrapped statues; lifted and totted cows and sheep, crib and shepherds and angels, and, moved enough potted poinsettias to fill a Christmas wonderland. When all had been done and the viejas had adjourned for their *cafecitos* — coffee, — Joy examined their handiwork. "Nice," she observed. "I guess it will do, but…." Then came that look. "I still think it needs… something."

Suddenly the princess assumed the Mikey-role. She took command. "We need some, no we need lots of boxes and paper bags and stuff… and…."

They were off. A stop here, a pick-up there, *Tio's* — Uncle's — shrimping nets, even Abuelo's weird garden hat that looked as though it came right out of an old Tarzan movie. And the princess led the way.

They whooped and hollered and seemed to pick-up speed and intensity with every minute. They drew a crowd of young followers, fellow crusaders. "We're on a mission for God," declared Katerina Joy and the cry was picked-up by each new crusader, who, before he or she could join the mission, had to spit on his or her palm and shake the spit-lubricated palms of the Gang of Four and swear a "blood oath" never to reveal what they were about to do.

Geraldito's contingent was discharged to shake the bushes and explore the hedges around St. Theresa's; Daniel and his troops canvased Schenley Park; the Princess and Miguelito and their squad went down Red Road, made a quick left and before most of their pint-sized adventurers could figure it out, they were in the university's arboretum. Everywhere, they were on a mission for God.

Two hours later, back at the church, they renewed their sacred blood oath by again spitting on their palms and shaking each other's hands, committing each to the other to go to their graves (or at least college) never telling their secret. Then, they released their captives and headed home to prepare for *Noche Buena* — Christmas Eve — and the *Misa del Gallo* — Midnight Mass — even though it would start at nine o'clock).

So it was that Father Mark, having finished his own family's early Noche Buena and a last minute hospital call, barely had time to rush in the sacristy door, pull on his vestments, arrange the altar servers and ministers, march them around the side of the church, and to the refrains of *O Come, O Come Emmanuel,* begin the entrance procession.

From his first step into the church Mark could feel it. Something strange. Wonderful. A buzz. A murmur. It was almost palpable, like a static of people whispering to each other all about the same thing. As he approached the altar and Christmas crib he understood. They were everywhere – flitting among the poinsettia, standing atop cows and shepherds, nestled on Mary's arm and on Joseph's staff, three of them sharing the manger's straw with the Baby Jesus. Butterflies – monarch and red and lacewing, painted ladies and leopards, blues and yellows, and some so variegated that you can't describe them. And, if truth be told, more than a few moths.

As Mark reached the altar's steps, he turned to Miguelito, the thurifer. (Hey, it's a Catholic thing. The thurible is used for burning incense and the thurifer is the one who carries the thurible.) As Mark spooned incense over the burning coals and a cloud of smoke encompassed them, Miguelito nodded toward the butterfly-filled sanctuary. "It's Christmas and Easter all in one, Father," he said. "It's a Christmas mitzvah... a simple, quiet act of kindness, a minor miracle in which God chooses to be secret."

And so, Father Mark began his sermon saying. "Merry Christmas, everyone. I see... I see... I see we have a mitzvah – a simple, quiet act of kindness, a minor miracle in which God chooses to be secret.

"Tonight we celebrate the Mitzvah of Christmas, God's gentle gift of Peace and Joy. Peace to all men and women and Joy, Joy that is complete."

$\mathcal{L}$ittle Havana –
It's Not Guatemala

One of my earliest heroes was the English martyr Thomas Becket. In the T. S. Eliot play *Murder In The Cathedral*, Becket preaches the Christmas 1170 sermon in Canterbury Cathedral and describes the intimate connection between Christmas and the Eucharist (Communion).

Becket and Eliot were both too theological for this gathering and so I thought I would turn to two friends to share an idea.

◄○►◄○►◄○►◄○►◄○►◄○►◄○►◄○►◄○►◄○►◄○►

Dennis O'Brien was not the proverbial "happy camper." At best, Christmas would be a "working holiday." At worst... he didn't even want to think of things getting any worse.

Six weeks ago he had been happily preparing for an Advent tour of mission out stations in the mountains of Guatemala's Huehuetanango Province.

Then word came that his mother was sick, and he returned to Miami — "just in case" — for her by-pass surgery.

In his downest moments, he felt like lashing out at her. Widowed since his early teens, she stubbornly refused to move from home in the mid-60s and never stopped complaining about "those Cubans" when the neighborhood became "Little Havana." She objected to his vocation and was furious about his going to mission. Now, he couldn't help but feel that she had secretly, subconsciously, planned this whole "medical emergency" just so that he would be home for Christmas.

Despite his most selfish inclinations, he bit his tongue

and told his brothers to stay home with their families those first days after surgery; he'd take care of Mom. Then came the doctor's evaluations — Mom would be fine but it would probably be late March or early April before she could really care for herself.

Consigned to his fate, a dejected Dennis offered his services to the local parish. After all, he had grown-up there — graduated, as practically the only "Anglo," from the parish school, been an altar boy in the church, and come back to celebrate his First Mass of Thanksgiving.

Under other circumstances, "home for the holidays" would have been enjoyable but this wasn't home any longer. After ordination he avoided language school — having grown-up in "Little Havana," he only had to slow his rapid Cuban clip and absorb the local Guatemalan idioms. His first assignment had been to Huehuetanango and he was *en su casa* — at home. But at six foot four inches, with the blonde-haired, blue-eyed frame of a college tight end, he often resembled a clerical Jonathan Swift in the land of the Lilliputians.

The men, women, and children of the scattered villages that made up his mission were struggling, hardworking, proud Indigenous people who had been oppressed for years. Local catechists had been murdered because they had shared the Christmas "Good News"; time and again Indigenous communities had been forced off lands they had carved from the jungle and made productive, so that wealthy land owners tied to the military could take over; and hunger and illness claimed a daily, generation-to-generation toll on the people. But the Gospel survived. Hope continued, sometimes if only in and for the children.

Little Havana was a long way – in miles and culture – from the mountains of Guatemala. Dennis may have grown-up in one place but now his spirit lived in another. The adjustment, even if he had been away for only three years, was difficult. Traffic, lights, noise; a parish so clerical and far removed from the struggles of the people; choirs and robes and collections. Yet it wasn't all bad. Denny lived in the neighborhood, in the home in which he had been reared, and, as far as the parish was concerned, at least he celebrated the Spanish Masses, worked in the school, did some counseling, and had been assigned the altar boys.

Then, surprise! Dennis met Mikey. The kid was a trip. His parents alternately called him "Miguel" and "Miguelito" but to Dennis he seemed a perfect "Mikey." Turned out he lived almost right next door. A whirlwind of motion that didn't seem to understand the meaning of "stop" or "be still." And this altar boy virtually breathed questions:

"Why do we have to wear these robes?"

"What are all those statues for anyway?"

"Why don't the other priests live in real houses like

you do and let the homeless live in that big place?"

And going – morning, noon and night – Mikey was a blur of activity, frequently stopping his bike at Dennis's home or in front of the church just long enough to announce a destination – another "mission" adventure. The beach. A homeless shelter. A family whose son was with the Marines in Somalia and for whom Miguelito would write letters. An old man there. A single mother here. Denny was fascinated by the boy dynamo. Did I say "fascinated"? I meant "frustrated" – at least when it was "prepare the altar boys for Midnight Mass time."

Miguel would arrive late. Somebody was sick and he had to take them food from the *cantina* – the neighborhood restaurant. Then he would squirm through practice, and "have to leave early" – he had promised that he would babysit so Señora Theresa could do Christmas shopping. In desperation, Dennis assigned Mikey the one task he was certain the boy would not screw-up: no candles to drip wax, no bells to drop, no (God forbid) incensors from which to spill hot coals. Cross bearer – walk in, don't fall asleep, walk out.

But through it all, there had seemed to Dennis to be a sense that Mikey had a most special understanding, better than most, of just what was happening. One afternoon, as practice ended, the boy's questions started again.

"Father, I don't understand. If we're celebrating the

birthday of Jesus and you say that he really becomes alive in the Communion, every Mass should be special. And, why is it that so many people don't go to Communion, if it's really the Body and Blood of Jesus and if He wants to give Himself to us, and if that's why we have Mass, and if we believe that? The way I see it," observed the pint-sized theologian, "the only reason for the first Christmas was so that later on Jesus could have the Last Supper and give us the chance for Communion all the time so that he could always be with us. Isn't that what it's all about? I think so," he said with an air of finality that gave his own answer.

Miguelito's questions cut right to the soul. They took Denny back to Guatemala, to the open-air-crying-babies-everything-in-chaos Christmas Masses of the past three years. No frills. People came together out of the struggles of their lives to pray and be strengthened by the Living Christ in the Eucharist. It was all so much simpler and Mikey had hit upon it.

As Christmas drew closer, Dennis's internal turmoil continued to bubble – early Masses; morning starts of mother's day; hospital calls. He had volunteered to celebrate Mass in the downtown home of Mother Teresa's Missionaries of Charity. Mikey had actually saved him some effort – he had offered to take his ubiquitous bike to one of those Flagler Street restaurants that sold *comida por libra* – food by the pound – for mother's evening meals.

(She complained about it being Cuban and not liking it and "too much rice and beans" even as she devoured it like a hungry high school footballer. But Dennis loved it and she would have complained anyway.) It had actually been Mikey's idea — the particular restaurant at least. Seems that he was already running a free delivery service for a lot of the *viejos* — old folks — in the neighborhood.

In all of this, Dennis longed for Guatemala. But it was Christmas Eve now and there was much to do. Mother was still ensconced; his brothers and their families would arrive at noon on Christmas Day with dinner and all the trimmings. And, even though she could get around, her prejudices had refused the invitation to join Miguelito's family for *Noche Buena* — the traditional Cuban Christmas Eve. Dennis went alone.

It was loud and crowded. With so many people milling about in Mikey's small two-bedroom home, Denny was never able to get a precise count of just how many there were for dinner. It must have been the entire family — aunts, uncles and cousins. Everyone but Mikey. In all of the confusion, the boy managed to slip in unnoticed just as everyone was finishing dinner and with barely enough time to change before accompanying Dennis on the three block walk to the church.

Mikey explained that it had been a "very, very busy day — Christmas Eve and all that." He had been at the *comidas por libras* — meals by the pound — restaurant first thing that morning, helping the man prepare all the Noche Buena meals of roast part that families had ordered. After the clean-up, he used his bike to take all the leftovers to some families with lots of kids that could really use them. It had been a "very, very busy day," the boy repeated. Finally, the priest and Miguelito were at the church.

Long before Mass, the place was alive with activity — choirs warming up, instruments being tuned, ushers, people arriving early to be sure to save their own places and some for the family late-comers, and the usual Christmas Eve drunk or two wandering around outside.

Everything seemed to being going pretty well. Dennis supervised preparations.

Incense was smoking, holy water bucket and aspergillum (the holy water sprinkler) ready; altar boys set in red cassocks and white surplices, complete with big red bows at the collar.

At last, "*Todos listos?* — Everyone ready?"

"*Uno, dos, tres! Vamanos!* — One, two, three! Let's go!" — Out the sacristy door, around the side of the church, up the aisle.

The liturgy had barely begun when Dennis glanced over to the second row of altar boys seated against the sanctuary wall. Mikey was sound asleep. And could he sleep! Through the choir, the sermon, the incense.

Then, just as the old pastor paused before starting the consecration, Mikey woke — sliding from his chair to his kneeler, alert and aware. He managed to stay that way until seconds after the chalice was returned to the altar and then, amazingly, Mikey fell asleep in a kneeling position.

Dennis was pretty certain he was the only one who realized what had happened with the kid, who somehow pulled a second miracle by waking again right on time to march forward for Communion. The priest almost lost control to laughter as the boy approached, one palm extended over the other, and winked as he received the consecrated host.

When Dennis had completed the distribution of Communion, as he was cleaning the sacred vessels, he noticed something especially unusual — Mikey was still kneeling, eyes closed. But he wasn't sleeping this time. Somehow, Dennis understood, Mikey was praying; he had received Communion but now he was "in communion."

In the end, as Dennis gave Mikey a promised ride home, the boy began to apologize. "I'm sorry, Father. I didn't mean to fall asleep."

"That's okay, Miguel," the priest answered. "You had had a full day already and, besides, you were awake for the important parts."

"Merry Christmas."

2017

Christmas With 'The Beard' At Titanic

Some months ago, my friend Father Scott Harris insisted that I had to share a story – really never previously told to anyone – with Sister Grace of the Maryknoll Sisters' Contemplative Community or, as I alternately call them, "the Cloister" and "the Power House" and "The Chalet."

I've always believed in the power of stories and, as God and too many of you know, I've told more than my fair share. Nevertheless, tonight, two stories that I've told only three or four times over the forty-two and more than fifty years since the original events. They are so personal (and sometimes painful) that I pray you will pardon my sharing them with you as part of a story.

◄о►◄о►◄о►◄о►◄о►◄о►◄о►◄о►◄о►◄о►◄о►

The beards made the evening. The night, if we want to be precise. Not Mark's particularly, although its genuine snow-whiteness would have been the envy of many a Santa. His had started with Movember — No Shave November — and he's considering waiting until Super Bowl Sunday (when Mike Flynn traditionally takes down his Christmas decorations) before looking for his razor.

But that wasn't THE BEARD.

Miquelito, Miguel, Mikey, or as so many of his college friends now called him, "Mig," took that honor hands down. (But, we'll return to THE BEARD in a moment. First you must understand the evening.)

Although, like the host of the biblical wedding feast who didn't know just who might accept his invitation or if he'd be left sitting alone at the Titanic bar, this was still one of Mark's favorite nights of the year. It had started more than a generation ago when he was working in a small, very poor immigrant parish in which sons and daughters were the first generation to go to an American college or university.

Now it's a well-kept but universally recognized secret that — even if their shadow hasn't crossed a church threshold since September — college kids join their families for *Misa del Gallo* — Midnight Mass — because it's a guaranteed opportunity to see all of their friends. And, "21 and Unlimited Wings," as the December 21 event was advertised, had been an on-going attempt to reconnect students with their home parish and the Church. The rules were simple: eight p.m. until whenever; unlimited sodas and all the chicken wings any human could consume, and, if you were twenty-one or older, no more than two beers no matter who's driving. And, *por supuesto* — of course, Mark picked up the tab.

The date never varied, the Titanic was an easy location and never knowing who might attend, Mark anticipated it with the same enthusiasm as his smallest altar servers looked forward to Christmas gifts.

◄O►◄O►◄O►◄O►◄O►◄O►◄O►◄O►◄O►◄O►◄O►

The ebb and flow of the crowd that night never

seemed to ebb when, 'round 'bout 10 and right-on-time by student schedules, THE BEARD wandered, strolled, strutted in.

Somewhere north of six foot two inches, a solid two-hundred-plus, topped by a thick, longish, brush-cutted brown-blonde mat that flowed down to a fashion model-perfect beard, Miguelito worked his way through the crowd and grabbed Mark in an *abrazo* – hug – worthy of a professional wrestler.

For years Mark had confidently declared that he wasn't "getting old; it's just that these kids keep getting younger and younger." Now, suddenly, some of these kids had grown up and grown beards.

The priest's brain was caught in a whirlpool of memories: the four-year-old Miquelito pulling feathers from his Christmas-gift Indian war bonnet and presenting them to the Baby in the altar Nativity scene and destroying Mark's homily; Mikey the neighborhood terror on his Three Kings bike; Miguelito the leader of a band of Christmas tree salesmen taking care of the poorest of the poor; Miguel, adopting a whole chapter of Sigma Chis at the University of Miami.

Now, for the first time, Mark realized how much Miguelito – or Mig as he was introducing himself to everyone – was a young man comfortable in his own skin and owning the room.

By eleven-thirty, most of the evening's crowd had

wandered – Ubered – off to Brickell and Winwood and Mark found himself in the incomprehensible situation of sharing a pitcher with his former altar boy. A senior with an extra year to go in his five-year Bio-Medical Engineering program, Mig had completed almost all of his major courses and was deep-diving into – of all things – Philosophy and (hold your breath) Religion. "Who'd da thunk it, Father."

"Miguel, Mikey, Mig… We're sitting at the Titanic sharing a pitcher and wings. We've known each other your whole life. At least here, drop the 'Father' bit. Please, dude."

That one caught Mig by surprise.

"So, what…?"

"Try starting with 'Mark' and, if that doesn't fit, you'll figure it out."

"So, Ma…" His tongue froze somewhere between "Ma" and "rk,"

"So, dude. My roommate was going to take this religion course on Death and he didn't want to sit through Death with a bunch of Religion and Philosophy nerds and convinced me…. It's amazing. Write your own obituary, read Kafka, and Camus and Pope Francis and Kubler Ross. Have you ever heard of her?"

"Yes," Mark smiled, neither interrupting nor giving voice to the thought "Way before you were born."

"And, since I'm way ahead on my bio-engineering

courses, I'm thinking of a double major – either Religion or Philosophy. Next semester I have courses on the Philosophy of Science and What Makes Us Human."

Mark focused all of his inner strength on being quiet, relishing the excitement of his young friend, allowing a budding enthusiasm to engulf both of them. "It's like a whole new world's opening up. Did you study all this stuff. I mean, not just the God questions and faith things – I know that's seminary – but the Philosophy of Knowledge and what makes us human?"

Mark soaked it all in. And, in almost typical Miguelito fashion, Mig was on a tear. Naming philosophers. Describing papers he had worked on. The challenges his professors had presented.

"I mean I think my new favorite word is WHY."

Not suddenly, but, yes suddenly, Mig shifted positions and moods – somehow simultaneously stretching out his six-foot two-inch frame while becoming even more intense. "Yeah. That's it. My favorite word lately has been WHY.

"In fact, come to think about it, it's something I've never asked you. Mark, why? You're smart. I've heard you preach and teach. You've got a doctorate in psychology. You speak Spanish. You could do just about anything. Why?"

Mark was caught. In the Titanic of all places and with wings and a not quite empty pitcher in front of him, he was being asked THE QUESTION. Carefully pouring out equal shares, he collected himself long enough to try to frame almost fifty years into a cogent answer.

"Hombre, let me answer with a few quick stories.

"During my first year of law school, a fraternity brother was killed in Vietnam. It was that time. A lot of young guys were dying or having their lives destroyed. His death just started me thinking, questioning, asking many of the same questions you're asking. Asking 'Why?' Ultimately, the response of St. Francis – 'Lord, make me an instrument of your peace' – just seemed to make sense. Not that I be a priest but that I try to be a peace maker.

"Now, I don't always have the best of luck in that. I wasn't sure that it – being a priest – was what I wanted but God has a helluva sense of humor. So, in September 1973, I was studying in Santiago, Chile, when there was a military coup. Somehow, five days later I managed to get myself arrested and thrown into prison – a story for another pitcher of beer, but not tonight 'cause we've both got to drive. And, this is where God gets the laugh because it's when and where he showed Himself to me as the Living Christ.

"As I recall, we were more than one-hundred-and-fifty men and boys penned-up in the locker room of the National Football Stadium. One afternoon, as we were being fed our daily cup of beans and a hard roll,

I watched a young soldier — maybe younger than you, Miguel, probably a Mapuche Indian — keeping guard over the prisoners — again, many of them your age. These kids had been locked up for a week; many of them faced an almost certain death or incarcerations that would be living deaths. They were jonesing for a smoke and kept begging that young kid-soldier for just one cigarette.

"And that's when everything changed for me. The guard just marched his route — fifteen or twenty paces one way, about face, and fifteen or twenty paces back, over and over. And, slowly reaching into his shirt, pulled out a cigarette, lit it, and threw it away — at the feet of the prisoners. Over, and over. Pull out a cigarette. Light it. Throw it away. Finally, when the order came for the prisoners to return to the locker room, he reached into his shirt one more time, grabbed what must have been an almost full pack and threw them all at the prisoners.

"To this day, I believe that in that young soldier I saw the Living Christ. In that simple act of kindness, I saw what it means to be a peacemaker. From that moment, I've never really had a choice. Why? Because...."

"Whoa!" exhaled Miguel.

"But Mikey, God's got a weird sense of humor. Man plans and God laughs His butt off — of course, that is if God has a butt. He wanted to make sure that I understood He generally shows Himself in simple acts. So, just weeks before I was ordained, a truly special friend – a Maryknoll Sister with whom I had worked in Chile – came back to the states for my ordination. Carla's mother had been opposed to her vocation and never accepted it, hadn't communicated with her in forever. Carla spent years in counseling working through her mother's rejection and when she came back, she went to visit, only to discover that her mother was in the advanced stages of Alzheimer's disease and didn't even recognize her. When I saw her, after she got back from visiting her mother, Carla was truly broken. There were no words of consolation.

"So, I called my friend Mary Tanner, whose husband had died less than two years earlier, leaving her with sons seventeen and sixteen, a fifteen-year-old daughter, and four-year-old twin girls. 'I'm bringing over a friend. She's hurt and broken. We'll be there in 15 minutes.'

"Now, when you walk into the Tanner home it's a straight line from the front door to the dinner table on the other side of the living and dining rooms. As we walked in, Mary, seated at the opposite side of the table, turned, pulled out a bottle of Scotch from the cabinet behind her, put it on the table, and told the kids 'Get glasses and ice.' Then this tiny wisp of a woman grabbed Carla in the most wonderful hug you've ever seen. And, in that embrace of two of God's broken people, I saw again the Living Christ.

"Why, mi amigo? Why? Because it just makes sense.

Why? Because we make plans and God laughs.

"Why, because I've learned to see Him in the little and the unexpected things, not where I want Him to be — but in the stable and in the unexpected, where He waits for us. In shepherds that smell like their flocks, before wise men and kings. God laughs.

"Why? Because simple acts of kindness can become both ordinary and extraordinary. Because God has made us 'a little less than the angels' and we are His 'unfinished perfections' and He invites us to proclaim peace and heal with a hug. Why? Because God simply loves us 'now and now and now'….

"It just all makes sense. And, in some strange way, every day becomes a Christmas gift.

"Drink up, Dude.

"But, one last thing, Miguelito. Thank you. Thank you for your 'Whys' and thank you for letting me tell my story. I'll see you on Christmas Eve.

"Now, let's blow this firetrap.

"Merry Christmas, Barbudo. Or is it Barbarossa?"

"Merry Christmas, Santa Mark."

2010

Miguelito, the Magus

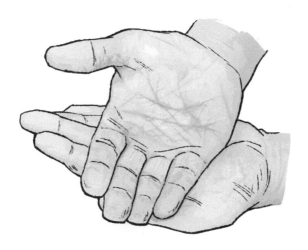

As an introduction, please allow me to note that during last Sunday's dialogue homily we had an intense discussion of apocryphal gospels, local or regional accounts of the Christ that were not universally accepted, and as a result, may not be well known to many of you.

An Eighth Century apocryphal account of the Magi has only recently been translated from ancient Syriac by a Catholic scholar from Harvard. It set me a'thinkin.

◄O►◄O►◄O►◄O►◄O►◄O►◄O►◄O►◄O►◄O►◄O►

Some time ago (although he was quite sure when), Miguelito decided that his grandparents were "quirky" even though he wasn't quite certain what quirky meant. He wasn't even sure when or where he ran across the word. All he knew was that "quirky" felt like an apt description.

Although he was still too young to really understand the entire Castro/Cuba/exile thing, he knew that *Abuelo* was studying to become a doctor when he left school and moved to Miami and spent the rest of his life working construction in order to provide for *Abuela, Papi,* and *Tio.* Papi often said that Abuelo was brilliant, a "Renaissance man," in love with Abuela and family, books, and learning. But, Miguelito thought him quirky because of the way he peppered his speech with unfinished sentences – "when in Rome," "if the shoe fits," *"ni chicha ni lemonada,"* and "O ye of little faith…."

And Abuela, oh Abuela. Mikey wasn't sure but he thinks that from before he could speak, he was afraid to misspeak in Abuela's presence. For example, he liked school. Liked it a lot, really liked it. Enjoyed it. Really enjoyed it. Appreciated and really appreciated school. But he didn't "love" school. After all, to say he "loved school" anywhere in earshot of his grandmother would have drawn "the eye" – that look of disapproval that left you either melting or quaking or both. She was, after all, as she would readily inform you, an *alumna* – never an *alumnus*, or God-forbid, *alumni*, of *El Convento del Sagrado Corazon de las Religiosas del Sagrado Corazon* – an alumna of the Convent School of the Religious of the Sacred Heart – and there she learned "Words are special. They have meaning. They should be used precisely."

Oh, she'd also inform you that because she had learned as a child to float effortlessly from "perfect English to perfect Spanish – without a trace of an accent," she would never tolerate "Spanglish."

Wednesdays, which were always spent at his abuelos' home because it was his parents' "date night," were the epitome of grandparental quirkiness. Abuela called Wednesday "Prince Spaghetti Day" – even though she always served *boliche* – Cuban pot roast – and Abuelo

230

always asked, "Did you learn everything in school today or do you have to go back tomorrow?" And dinner would be spent questioning Mikey about everything he had studied during the preceding week, with Abuela rounding out the conversation with a thorough review of vocabulary words and detailed explanations of their meanings, origins and usage.

That is why, for example, Mikey would never say he "loved school." He had been lectured more than once as a child: "You love people – those who can return your love. If it cannot love you back, you like it." Abuela would tolerate – but barely – the exception of cats and dogs (and maybe *Tio's* – Uncle's – parrot, but that was still in doubt).

Wednesdays had a ritual entirely their own. After school: homework, boliche, followed by flan and accompanied by intense questionings about school and classes and what he had learned. Then, on a giant sofa between his grandparents, Miquelito would read – out loud, sometimes haltingly, sometimes with ease; sometimes material of his choosing, sometimes Abuela would pick a book or article. Words he did not recognized were circled, written, sounded out, and explained.

Then on the first Sunday of Advent while browsing through his favorite book store, Mikey found a work he knew he had to read. (By the way, he knew he was browsing because Abuelo taught him "women shop, men buy and smart people browse — walk slowly through an area of interest and think about what they see." There it was with every Cuban-American child's second-to-Santa Claus favorite characters on the cover, and short — only a hundred pages, and lots of pictures: *The Revelation of the Magi: The Lost Tale of the Wise Men's Journey to Bethlehem.*

Mikey had to sound out the second word of the title and struggled through others. But he knew that he just had to have it and that from first to last page it would consume Wednesday nights.

In fact, even before Miguelito, Abuela seemed to understand that this little book was going to change many things. "*Aye, mijito, que ideas mas extranas dice este professor* — Oh what strange ideas this professor has," she exclaimed as she reviewed the cover.

And so, the revelations unraveled. They were wise men and kings from the land of Sirh on the extreme east of the world, at the shore of the Great Ocean. They were Zaharwandad, Hormizd, Atazp, Arsak, Zarwand, Aribo, Artahsisat, Astanbozan, Mirhuq, Ahsiras, Nasardih, and Merodak — descendants of Seth, the third son of Adam and Eve. Travelling from Sirh in huge caravans, they were not magicians or astrologers, or even priests. In the language of Sirh, they were *magi* — because "in silence, without a sound [they] glorified God and prayed. In silence and in the mind [they] glorified and prayed to the exalted and holy majesty of the Lord of Life."

By the end of that first night reading, Mikey was captivated and his abuelos enthralled. During the second week of reading they discovered that the journey began at the Cave of Treasures of the Mysteries of the Life of Silence on the Mountain of Victory, where the secret of God's eternal love for his people had been preserved first by Adam, then Seth and then his descendants, the magi, through the generations.

On the second Saturday of Advent, Mikey did something he had never done before, had never before imagined doing: He went to his abuelos' home "to read." And on Sunday, as he sat in the altar boy's chair during ten a.m. Mass, when Father Mark began to speak of the Epiphanies to the shepherds and the "Three Wise Men," Abuela gave him one of her infamous silent looks that screamed *"No digas nada, ni una palabra...* Don't say anything, not a word...."

Over the following days, Mikey and his abuelos absorbed the Revelation. That a pillar of light more brilliant than the sun appeared at the Cave of Treasures of the Mysteries of the Life of Silence. As the magi knelt in silent prayer, with their hands outstretched as was their custom, angels of God descended and instructed them, "enter inside without doubt, in love, and see a great and amazing vision." On entering they found that the light had concentrated itself, and appeared to them in the bodily form of a small and humble human being, who greeted them, "Peace to you, sons of my hidden mysteries. Do not doubt the vision you have seen… that it appeared to you to concentrate its light in rays, or that it appeared to you in the form of a small, humble, and unworthy human because the inhabitants of the world cannot bear to see the glory of the only Son of the Father of majesty unless it appeared for them in the form of their world."

Mikey was completely captured by the magis' experience – that each had seen the Christ in his own way:

"I saw a light in which there were many images that were amazing…"

"I saw an infant who had unspeakable forms…"

"I saw a youth who did not have a form of this world…"

"I saw a human being who was humble, unsightly in appearance, and poor…"

"I saw a cross and a person of light who hung on it…"

"I saw that he went down to Sheol with force and all the dead rose and worship him…. "

"I saw that he ascended into glory, and he opened the graves, and he raised up the dead…" and "I saw him ascending to the heavenly height, and angels opening the gates of heaven before him…."

And when they left the Cave of the Treasure of the Mysteries the Silent Life, the light transformed itself into a star that only the magi could see in day and night. And how the light – the Star – eventually led the magi from Sirh to Bethlehem, where, unlike the traditional story Mikey had heard each year and celebrated on the Twelfth Day of Christmas, January 6, it was the Christ who gave himself to the magi – no gold, no frankincense, no myrrh. Rather a gift of profound and personal peace.

With Christmas still two weeks away, Mikey could no longer contain himself. Sure, he knew that it was a family tradition – a guy thing – for Abuelo, Papi, Tio and now Miguelito to do all their Christmas shopping on Christmas Eve. "But, Father Mark has to have this book. He just has to have it," he insisted. And so, for the first time ever, on the Third Sunday of Advent, Father Mark received his first-ever Gaudete Sunday gift with the urgent instruction "You absolutely have to read this right away."

And he did. From cover to cover before the sun went down, including Miguelito's hand-written note: "Father, Abuela received a letter today from the Maryknoll Sisters. It says,

'No matter where we live or what we do, we are given the opportunity to meet Christ in the people we encounter along life's way. On a bus, in a classroom, at the home of a friend, in the grocery store – that is where we find the Christmas crib in the world today.'"

Added Miguelito, "I think that is the Revelation of the Magi: Jesus shows Himself to us as we need Him and as He knows we need Him, and as He needs us to help others, not as a baby in the manger." And Miquelito included a simple bookmarker with two quotes. One from an unknown Maryknoll Sister on Mission:

"With empty hands but grateful hearts...

I earnestly beg the Christ Child to transform into a golden gift my Christmas wish for you –

A vision of God that will make you eager to guide others to the place of vision;

A vision of yourself that shall give you charity for the weakness of others;

A vision of others that shall reveal to you their virtues more than their faults;

A vision of life that shall make you eager to work, willing to endure, and patient in waiting, a master of self, and a servant of all."

And the other from Mother Mary Joseph, foundress of the Maryknoll Sisters:

'All of us – shepherds, Magi and ourselves – will soon meet at the Crib, where Jesus, newly born, has been placed by Mary, His Mother. And there we may catch some spark of Mary's humility, of Joseph's patience, the Magi's correspondence to grace, the shepherds' simple, ardent faith and the Divine Child's charity and selflessness.'"

It was, thought Mark, the perfect gift — the wish, the hope to find the Christ as he presents himself to us and not as we would want him to be.

<hr />

My Christmas prayer for each of you:

"May you catch some spark of Mary's humility, of Joseph's patience, the Magi's correspondence to grace, the shepherds' simple, ardent faith and the Divine Child's charity and selflessness."

Other Christmas Tales

Andrew ...

Other Christmas Tales

From the beginning, please let me point out that this year's Christmas story is not about any one "little person." Rather, he is a composite of many - at least two of whom are with us this evening.

It has been a year since we last gathered here. A year in which I have been especially moved by the role and person of the care giver. From the "Jewish mother" nurse who has taken such special care of the dying and who will work an "extra" tonight so that Christian wives and mothers can be at home with their families, to friends who have not enabled addicts and alcoholics but made it possible for them to recover. From the nun who constantly listens to the language of teenagers that would send others to the cloister and the parents of small children who correct without destroying developing personalities to the parents and family of one priest who simply encourage and tolerate so that so many of you might be here this evening.

I am reminded by last Sunday's Gospel that the Incarnation, the mystery of the Word of God becoming flesh and sharing our humanity, was possible only because Mary dared to say to the Angel, "Behold the servant of the Lord. Be it done unto me according to your word."

This is dedicated to all those care giving servants.

◄◦►◄◦►◄◦►◄◦►◄◦►◄◦►◄◦►◄◦►◄◦►◄◦►◄◦►

Andrew, "hereinafter known as...." (Isn't that a great legal phrase? I only use it because his father is a hotshot attorney.) Andrew, hereinafter known as "The Little Person," was confused.

In fact, this was probably the first time The Little Person had ever been confused.

And confused for any little person is a very strange feeling. For The Little Person it was — well — confusing.

He knew that Christmas was coming: "Ho-Ho" and all that. He had helped "Pop-Pop" string lights at his grandparents' home and had declared confidently that his own home was "the most beautiful in the whole wide world." Andrew sorta understood that life followed a well-established order — Thanksgiving, Ho-Ho and Christmas, Daddy's then Mommy's birthdays, and finally his own, which is, he could say when asked, "in March," though he still wasn't exactly certain when — even what — March is.

It was this "Christmas thing" that was so confusing.

He had been told with almost unrelenting frequency that Christmas was "Baby Jesus' birthday." And he knew that must be right because every time someone new would stop-by to see the Christmas decorations and he would respond to his parents' question, "What is Christmas?" and he responded "Baby Jesus' birthday," everyone would smile and tell him how good or how smart or even how good and smart he was.

But for The Little Person birthdays were supposed to be observed with pool parties and cakes with icing and coconut chips. And there was no sign of any of these.

There was lots of Christmas, though. The whole house looked different — a decorated tree and a big plastic Santa Claus stuffed with rolled-up newspapers. That had been his job — scrunching up newspapers and helping Pop-Pop push them into every nook and cranny of Santa Claus' chest and arms and legs. There had been cooking, baking and gift wrapping, although it was readily apparent that none of this was actually for the

Baby Jesus. And it was supposed to be *His* birthday.

And there were Christmas cribs — at his own and his grandparents' homes. He had been alternately allowed to watch the careful placement of each piece — even put some of the cows and sheep in their places — and told, "Don't touch, Honey" each time he went back to observe his own handiwork. There were big cribs, too, in front yards and at churches. Tonight his own church was supposed to have a crib with *live animals* and people in costumes. *And a real baby, too.*

It was a time of much anticipation. Someone was always asking him, "Don't you remember last Christmas when...?" Of course, The Little Person would always answer "Yes" and the questioning grown-up's face would assume a confident "I-told-you-so" smile.

In fact, The Little Person really did not remember much about last Christmas — except that he had gotten a lot of toys from Ho-Ho at Pop-Pop's house, and on arriving at his own home on Christmas afternoon, he discovered that Santa Claus had, indeed, been there too. He could tell, not simply from the huge pile of gifts awaiting him, but from the crumbs on the once-full plate of Christmas cookies and the now empty glass of milk he had so carefully remembered to leave out for Ho-Ho.

But for the moment, it was time to get ready for Church. There was, he had heard his parents say, to be a Christmas Eve children's Mass. The Little Person was already decked out in new shoes, navy blue pants, white shirt and bright red — his favorite color — tie, with a Christmas-bright red sweater. His parents were still dressing as he sat contemplating the family Christmas crib. And this was where the confusion came.

Yes. He knew that Christmas was the birthday of the Baby Jesus. But, last Sunday The Little Person had paid particular attention in Church. Even before Mass began his mother had warned, "the birds outside are watching and will report everything to Santa Claus." So he had been very good. Perhaps that is why he heard the priest explain that the real heroes of Christmas were Joseph and Mary. The priest used words like "sacrifice" and "humility" and "simplicity" and "service" - words The Little Person did not understand but knew were important - to describe the mother and father of Jesus. He said that, if it had not been for their doing what God wanted, there would be no Christmas because the Baby Jesus could not have been born.

The Little Person was truly confused, as only an almost-four-year-old can be confused: Mary and Joseph are the really important people but it is Jesus' birthday and he, Andrew, was the one expecting all of the gifts. Something wasn't right about all of this. And, as only an almost-four-year-old can, he felt some profound moral imperative to correct this situation.

So it was that Andrew, The Little Person, came to his

decision.

When his parents descended the staircase, they found The Little Person ready to go, pillow case in hand. They really did not think much of the additional costuming. It had become a common practice for him to take a pillow to church for those times when he would fall asleep — especially at the adult masses.

The ride to the church was brief — only about five minutes — and when they arrived, The Little Person and his parents found a large number of families already gathered around the outside "living Christmas crib." In the familiar setting of the church property, Andrew maneuvered his way to the front. He wanted to be certain to see everything that was happening.

Then, just as the priest began to intone "The Proclamation," The Little Person opened his pillow case and pulled out a huge, little-handful bouquet of red, white, and pink chrysanthemums, the flowers that earlier that day his father brought home for his mother and she had left uncut and unarranged in the kitchen sink. Dropping the pillow case, he walked full-square into the manger scene, flowers in hand. Turning to the persons of the Blessed Mother and Saint Joseph, he extended the make-shift bouquet and declared in a most confident voice: "Here. These are for you. I have decided that the Baby Jesus and I already get enough gifts at Christmas and somebody should give you something. Because you are the ones who really give us Christmas."

Mary held the flowers and the Christ Child. Saint Joseph just looked at the simple, make-shift bouquet and smiled. No one had ever given him flowers before – whether as Saint Joseph or as his real self. And, as The Little Person's mother and father attempted to snatch him out of the manger where they were not quite sure whether he did or did not belong, the priest just threw up his hands, smiled, turned to the congregation and said, "Merry Christmas. Peace be with you."

2000

Bead Clicking and Prayer

Twenty-five years ago, at the time of my ordination, Father Frank Meccia was my spiritual director, mentor, and one of my closest friends in Maryknoll. Not without reason, I called him "old weird Frank." A generation or more before it was fashionable, he had a pierced ear and wore his extremely thinning reddish hair in a pseudo-Afro. Talented and imaginative, he seemed to function in a world far distant from the one in which most of us live.

In his room, he always displayed a small Nativity set and explained that it was because we must remember that the message of Christmas cannot be limited by time or geography.

As told by Frank, on the day of my ordination he went to visit a Maryknoll Sister who was close to death. Years earlier, he had made a small banner for her. It read simply, "Butterflies count not the days nor the hours and have time enough." He says that, on leaving, he told her that, because her death was imminent, he was taking the banner back and giving it to me. According to his tale, she responded, "That's alright, Frank. Tell Skip 'Hi' for me and that I am praying for him."

A few years later, after officiating at the funeral of

a teenager who died in a terribly tragic automobile accident, I gave the banner to his family.

Until recently, I had not thought of it for years.

For weeks I had planned to write, "This Christmas story is dedicated to the memory of a grand lady." But I'm pretty sure that Gladys − the grandmother of that teenager − would just laugh at the idea of being called a grand lady. As politically incorrect as it is, "A great old dame" would be more appropriate.

And, it is dedicated to Mark Reeves, who often celebrated this liturgy with us and is now in Rome studying for his own ordination. Some of us have an investment in keeping his feet to the fire.

◄O►◄O►◄O►◄O►◄O►◄O►◄O►◄O►◄O►◄O►◄O►

Here's a quick lesson for any of you who are planning to become "professional religious" − those of you who are thinking of becoming priests. (Listen carefully, Mark.) Whenever someone says "I just thought I would warn you…" forget schedules and hold on tightly because you're about to begin a rollercoaster ride.

The call − "Gladys has asked for you to stop by" − came the day before. I had met her two or three times. She had even been here (my parents' home) once for Christmas Eve Mass, but the truth is that I wouldn't have recognized her if I had fallen over her. And that Sunday afternoon I had more than enough on my schedule. But I made time. As I rang the doorbell at her son's home, I was figuring "in and out — 10 to 15 minutes at most."

That's when Gladys's son met me at the door with those infamous words "I thought that I'd better warn you... she's inside, waiting for you and doing her beads."

No. Gladys wasn't dying. She had fallen and fractured some vertebrae; she was in a lot of pain. The meds didn't work. He decided to bring her home so the family could keep track of her medicines and try to make her comfortable. The doctors said it would be about ten weeks and she'd just have to get through it.

Yes, there were some things she wanted to talk to me about. He wasn't sure that she was afraid of dying, but...

Somewhat forewarned I went inside. Gladys motioned me to a seat and her son and daughter-in-law quickly excused themselves. On a wall hung the banner — "Butterflies count not the days nor the hours and have time enough."

She recounted a "roll in the hay — that's what we called it in those days," that made her a single mother at fifteen, a tough life marked by years of alcohol abuse, sobriety for the last five years or so, and most remarkably, her conversion to Catholicism.

It seems that, while living in a retirement community on Florida's West Coast, she used to watch a priest "bring the bread to the old neighbor ladies" and decided "I want to get the bread." And so, she became a Catholic. It was, I thought to myself, a whole new theological category — "Faith Through Boredom and the Need for Company." With no catechism training and even less fanfare, Father Mike — like a cagey old fox protecting her young, she never disclosed his last name or the parish in which he worked — welcomed her into the Church.

She attended Mass pretty regularly and genuinely grew in Faith until injury and the need to be close to family brought her to Miami. Once ensconced in a new retirement community she tried to attend Mass but the priest there mocked her lack of "knowledge" of the Faith and even laughed at the way she prayed "the beads."

So it was that, after her accident, I was called in. Gladys needed reassurance that what she was doing was "OK." She told me, "I pray my beads all the time," and lifted her rosary to show me. But there was something in the way she said it. Something that gave the distinct impression that she meant just what she said — she prayed the beads and not the Rosary. I was quiet. There was no way I was about to enter a theological discourse with this crusty old lady. After all, she had already dismissed the last priest with the temerity to disagree with her. Then, between winces of intense pain, she lifted the plastic beads, explaining, "For each bead I talk to God and ask him to take care of the people I love and everyone who needs my prayers. I pray my beads."

Next she raised her other hand, displaying a broken plastic crucifix. "And I talk to my Jesus. I found him at a yard sale, at the bottom of a barrel. The next day I went back and tried to find his hands and feet. I even went through all the trash. But no luck. My Jesus. He's just as old and broken up as I am."

An hour flew by. At the end of our visit, we prayed together and I gave Gladys Communion and the Sacrament of the Sick.

A week later, the family called. Her pain had worsened. She was in the hospital. I visited the next day. Her pain was unrelenting and her mouth too parched for her to receive Communion. She grasped her broken, arm-less, foot-less Jesus and prayed, "Lord, I know that you are busy with so many people who need your help. But, if you can find a little time for me and take this pain away for a while, I would appreciate it."

This lady, who prayed not the Rosary but her beads, this crusty ole gal had a real understanding of Christmas — that God became Man in the Person of Jesus in order to enter into and share our broken humanity. That He did it for a time — a moment in history — *and it was time enough* for generations and generations hence. That the stable somehow shaped Him, made Him so approachable that we can tell Him just what we think and what we need — without special words or ceremony.

The last prayer of the Church each day is very simple:

"May the Lord grant us a restful night and a peaceful death." I prayed that night for Gladys's peace. For the end of her pain. And, the Lord granted our prayer.

I thought of Gladys and of butterflies and of the humanness of the Christ each time I tried to write this homily. The phone kept ringing — people in physical and emotional pain, people with wants and needs. The sound of never-ending traffic, sirens and horns and people losing patience on the expressway ramp into the shopping mall nearby all broke into my thoughts and interrupted my efforts. I thought of Frank Meccia at Maryknoll and Mark Reeves in Rome. And I prayed for them. I prayed for them, as I pray for you, that somehow we all come to appreciate that by the Mystery of His Moment in History the Eternal Son of the Eternal God has consecrated and made holy our moments.

I prayed for myself, and I prayed for all of you, that we might learn to live our moments — to enjoy our rollercoaster rides — by bringing the Christ of this night into the lives of all whom we meet. That we might live the moments of our lives encountering the Christ of this night in all whom we meet.

For, while butterflies count not the days nor the hours and have time enough, we have Christmas. And, surely, that is enough.

Santa's Missing,
Santa's Missing

This story has special significance for me. As I recall, I wrote it for the first Christmas Eve Mass I celebrated at my parents' — our — home. After Mass, I heard my father commenting to a friend, "I wonder where he got that."

And yes, the monastery and star and the fable of the star are real. You can visit them in Cuzco.

◄◦►◄◦►◄◦►◄◦►◄◦►◄◦►◄◦►◄◦►◄◦►◄◦►

It wasn't really a start. Perhaps best described as "a fast-slow awakening," as much a consequence of the barely perceptible brightening of the winter-grey sky as a response to the deepening cold which seemed to invade the room as the once roaring Yule logs in the massive hearth went from glowing embers to quiet ash. Slowly, with a mechanical precision developed over the course of generations, her hand fell from the arm of the familiar, well-worn chair to the table at her side. And, in a fashion so natural it no longer evoked the slightest thought on her part, a candle and match were extracted from within the dark recesses of the top most drawer. Match went to flint and flame to wick. In an instant the candle's light dispelled the darkness, and, as she moved to place the taper on its mantel stand, she caught her first glimpse of the fireplace clock.

"Ten fourteen," she thought to herself. "Dawn comes so late during North Pole winters." Then, just as the dark of the room was brightened by the candle's light, the sleep-fog of her own mind began to lift. Not just dawn. This was THE DAWN. This was Christmas morning.

And even as the realization settled in, Mrs. Clause began once more to appreciate one of the most unique and special aspects of Christmas at the North Pole – that Christmas begins there at the very moment it begins in the very first countries of the globe; but, there, at the crown of the earth, Christmas doesn't end until the last second of the last hour of Christmas Day in the last countries to see the sun set. At the North Pole Christmas Day is twenty-four hours and just a few more.

"Our day... our Christmas," she thought smiling to herself. "All ours, every hour, minute and second of it."

Bending down, she carefully placed new logs on the fire, making sure that they would catch quickly from the heat of the still red embers. Then, straightening herself, she began to realize that there was something somehow amiss. Looking around the broad sitting room, the lowest boughs of its decorated tree stretched out over the Nativity scene, she missed him.

Santa Claus. He wasn't there. In all the Christmases of all the years through so many centuries this was the first time that she had ever greeted Christmas morning without his laughter and the endless accounts of the activities of the previous night. Christmas morning and NO SANTA CLAUS.

Taking the candle from its mantel perch, she made her way through the sitting room. With the aid of its flickering flame she moved down corridors and around corners, past rows of dormitories and private apartments for the elves and their families, past the doll and sport and games and electronics workshops, through the massive Christmas Land dining room and into the kitchen. Pausing, she took her huge woolen cloak from its peg beside the rear door and made her way across the snow swept patio, the hem of her cloak whipping up its own miniature gales.

Finally, reaching the doors of the reindeer stables, she pushed them open and made her way inside, greeted by the familiar smells of apples and hay and the comfortable warmth that were the traditional welcoming rewards of Santa's ever-dedicated reindeer. All was as it should be. EXCEPT... except. NO REINDEER AND NO SANTA CLAUS.

Now she began to worry. No, not just worry. Now she was really becoming scared. Why this had never happened before. Oh sure. Sometimes he arrived very, very late, having barely beaten the first rays of sunrise off the beaches of the South Pacific. And there was the time that Rudolf and some of the others got into a couple of loaves of well-soaked rum cakes in Germany and had to "sleep it off" just a little somewhere south of Algeria. But that had been centuries ago and long before Santa revised his delivery system.

Ever since Columbus discovered America and all those other explorers had complicated things by discovering whole new continents, life had become just a little bit out of hand. And so, for efficiency's sake, he had established way-stations, with managers and everything. Santa had only to make stops at selected locations on each continent and in various countries. From there, the station managers took care of the rest. Of course, there were always the special stops that were a part of Santa's personal lists and that he always saved for himself – the orphanages and homes for the elderly; homes marked by tragedy or poverty; places filled more with despair than the hope and promise of Christmas. After that he might well be late, but he was always home on time to rouse her from her slumber there in her chair before the sitting room fire.

But this Christmas morning SANTA HAD NOT COME HOME.

She thought first to wake the elves, but what could they do?

Besides, they'd be waking in a couple of minutes, and if Santa and the reindeer arrived beforehand... Well, let them sleep. But, what to do?

Turning, she made her way back... closing the stable doors, across the patio, into the kitchen, hanging her cloak again. Through the kitchen and dining room, round the corridors and down hallways, and back into the sitting room with its now roaring fire, and on the other side of the tree with its red bows and baby's breath bouquets, sat Santa's huge and ancient desk.

She crossed to the desk with a new sense of purpose. The trip from the stable had set her mind. "Just like the song," she said to herself, remembering how in the closing minutes of yesterday's afternoon he sat there "making his list and checking it twice." They were to be his stops. Places where he wanted to make certain that even if there were no gifts, there would still be "the spirit of Christmas." And there, just as she had learned to expect after years of Christmas Eves, was the copy he had left for her. Santa's Christmas – 1985.

As she read it, suddenly there was no longer even the fear that had grown tighter and tighter during her journey from the stables.

Now, there was none of the joy of Christmas. Nothing.... Only a deep and growing pain, the pain of the loneliness of the Santa she so long loved, but whose secret Christmases she had never really known.

American soldiers on assignment in a Middle Eastern desert. Their Christmas would be tape-recorded letters from home and hot turkey dinners flown in by helicopter from a battleship in the Mediterranean.

Forty kids in a Bolivian home for handicapped children would awaken in the morning to the gifts of Christmas, thanks to Santa and two grade schools in Chicago.

Another home, if you could call it that. A mud shack with a grass roof, once the home of a father, mother and five children. Now its air hangs heavy with the feel of death from an African famine that has already claimed all but this mother and her oldest son - surviving on a few cups of grain a day.

A Veterans Administration hospital and the old man who had no one and nothing. Oh sure, for him and the hundreds like him in Veterans Hospitals there had been the usual parties earlier in the month, and the candy bars and tooth brushes and soap and shampoos. All dutifully given. But there would be no real Christmas — at least not until a young Jewish doctor, who had offered to cover so a Christian friend could have the holiday, would stop by, late in the afternoon just to watch TV and talk and end the visit — the first real human contact in months — with an honest "Merry Christmas."

And so the list continued. From continent to continent and time zone to time zone. SANTA'S CHRISTMAS. A SAD CHRISTMAS. Now the feelings were becoming mixed. His absence had her frightened for him; his twice-checked list made her sad.

Even as she stood there at the desk, Mrs. Santa Claus began to hear the sounds of morning coming to the North Pole. "Merry Christmases" rang out from every nook and corner and Christmas burst upon the Winter Wonderland. Then, just as quickly, the rumble started, and grew and rolled around corners and down corridors in a ceaseless, honest rumor: "Santa is gone. The reindeer never came home."

Within minutes the whole population of the North Pole was in panic. What to do? Where to look? How to look? Who would look? Santa was lost.

Everyone had ideas, each knew what he or she would do but, finally, it was Mrs. Claus' time to decide. Elves Jaime and Helene, Chang and Susan would each take parts of Santa's itinerary. From the network of North Pole short wave sets they would call all along the route of the previous night starting from both the beginning and the end points and either side of the middle. "Don't cause panic. Just say that you are conducting an efficiency check — what time did he pass through that area."

What would happen to Christmas? What would happen to the world, if the news ever got out that SANTA IS MISSING?

All the way stations were contacted; each reported "mission accomplished." Santa had been everywhere. And so, a second set of calls. This time to double check Santa's own special list. "Say nothing," the agents were told. "We don't want to get anyone upset. But could you see if, while he was in your area, he also made a special stop at..." The list included hospitals and homes, orphanages and old folks' residences, the lonely poor and the lonely wealthy, a place for run-aways and abandoned kids in Fort Lauderdale, a missioner's shanty town in the Philippines.

It took some time, but, again, the reports came back. "Santa's tasks had been completed and Christmas was everywhere." Everywhere but at the North Pole.

There was a panic at the North Pole. It was real. And Mrs. Claus began to share in it. Even as the last confirming calls were reported through the Christmas network, the sun was setting and Mrs. Claus was really frightened. So much so that for the first time in all the years of her marriage, she did something that she had never done before. She started to explore Santa's desk. First his calendar and then the papers on top of his desk. Lists. Lists of homes and names and gifts and needs. Lists of countries and villages. Lists of years and dreams, of the naughty and the nice. And in the drawers, more lists. List of children and adults, the sick and the athletic, the greatest and those who would one day die unknown and unnoticed.

Then, in the third drawer down on the left, something besides all the lists. Yellowed with age and brittle to the touch, they unfolded slowly – parchment sheets of line drawings and ancient commentaries in a language that had changed considerably over the centuries.

But the North Pole is a wonderland and just as all languages are magically translated, travel is instantaneous. And, in one and the same instant, Mrs. Claus understood and smiled and was magically transported to the place where now she knew Santa Claus to be.

◄o►◄o►◄o►◄o►◄o►◄o►◄o►◄o►◄o►◄o►◄o►

A strange crowd gathered at the end of the cobblestone street on which Mrs. Claus found herself. Above the heads of the short, brown-complexioned men and the women with their multi-colored shawls, sandal-shod feet and wind burned features, Mrs. Claus spied the antlers of Santa's magic sleigh team. The street looked so much like that in the parchment packet that Mrs. Claus knew precisely where she would find Santa Claus: in the *Capilla de la Navidad Eterna* – the Chapel of the Eternal Christmas.

To her left she found the entrance to the small, winding wooden staircase that led to the loft. It was barely passable but for the few rays of light that managed to penetrate the centuries of Peruvian dust that caked the windows. Yet it opened onto a wondrously ornate choir loft.

And there, between the stalls that had once been the spiritual homes of generations of Dominican friars, before the now dilapidated, silver-leafed pipe organ, curled up and peacefully sleeping atop a massive silver star that had been carefully laid into the wooden floor — THERE WAS SANTA CLAUS.

NO. She did not wake him. Not just yet.

Instead she settled herself quietly into one of the monastic stalls, beneath the large rose window, and from the packet in her hand, began to read the story of the Chapel of the Eternal Christmas.

It seemed, according to the legend, that hundreds and hundreds of years ago, when the monastery was home to countless monks with their shaved heads and long black and white robes, the Father Prior had agreed to accept into the protection of the cloister an Indigenous baby orphaned by one calamity or another and left victim of the Andean cold.

The baby's every wish was the command of the monks, and, with a fervor that sometimes was absent in their prayers, they did everything possible to make his life a happy one.

Yet, in the somber life of the monastery there was something missing. For most of the monks were too old to play — to really play — with the child. And, while he seemed a happy baby, the monks themselves felt guilty, as if, by the absence of other children in their hallowed halls, they had deprived *Pedrito* of playmates and something particularly important: play.

Strangely, everyone always seemed to remark what a special child he was — always smiling and always, always... happy.

As he grew and began to walk and talk, his happiness seemed mysteriously to grow with him. Then it was that the monks began to become more and more concerned, for now Pedro was beginning to talk - to talk about his friend and the games "we" played and the things "we" did together. That he would lie seemed beyond belief. But....

One day it happened. Brother Porter, charged with greeting all guests who rang the monastery's great exterior bell, responsible for ringing the resonant chapel bells that governed all life inside the monastery walls, burst in upon Father Prior in the his private study. "Come quick! A miracle."

The old Brother Bell Ringer was so excited he couldn't remember which language to speak and kept slipping from Spanish to his native Indigenous Quechua.

Down monastic corridors, robes flapping and rosary beads clanging, Brother Bell Ringer lead the abbot across the cloister into the chapel, down the main aisle, not even stopping to genuflect as he crossed before the altar, and up the finely polished steps to the choir monks' loft. Then, just three steps from the very top, he came to such a sudden halt that the Reverend Father ran full into him, losing whatever semblance of dignity the cleric might once have had.

There, before the two of them, square in the center of the choir loft... There was Pedrito and AND HIS FRIEND – PLAYING. Playing catch with a shining golden orb that bounced from choir stall to choir stall filling the air with a special glow... Playing with stars of silver that, when thrown into the air, would hang magically until called back to the hands of one of the children.

Filled with awe, the monks struggled both to regain their composure and to balance themselves on their knees on the staircase, for, in the wonder of the moment, they felt strangely like new Shepherds and new Magi whose task was not to pray but to adore.

Mother Christmas – Mrs. Santa Claus – sat quietly. It was, she thought, truly a wonder. The great silver star on which Santa Claus now slept marked the place of the miracle. Tradition has it that for many years, through the childhood of Pedrito, during those morning and afternoon hours when the monks themselves were busy about many things, the choir loft and, indeed, the entire chapel would ring with the joyous sounds of laughter – the laughter of the young and growing boy and the laughter of his friend. That is the reason for the silver star. It marks the place where, once again, the Son of God became a child – so that the world might ring with the laughter of children.

And, on this Christmas night, when his rounds had been completed, when all the gifts had been delivered, when his own special visits – to those most in need of the healing Spirit of Christmas had been made – Santa Claus came here – to the Chapel of the Eternal Christmas, so that he, too, might remember that Christmas is ultimately for the children, that they might ever remember that God became a child so that children might forever laugh.

Of He Can Do It . . .

When he was very young, my nephew, Blaine, had an imaginary dog named Blacky. As children, many of us had imaginary friends.

Over the years, as a priest preparing for this evening, I've often enjoyed the exploits of my imaginary friend – Miguelito. He's been a thought provoking, insight and amusement providing, and very personal Spirit of Christmas as he's made his appearances here through the course of the last ten or twelve years.

Mikey has been a regular part of our Christmas celebrations. To the best of my ability to calculate, he's somewhere between about seven — the age at which he made his first appearance in one of our Christmas homilies — and about twenty or fifty-eight. I'm not exactly sure. Miguelito's age has always been a reflection of his wisdom and his ability to put the mysteries of Christmas into perspective for me.

So, we spent a little time recently over a couple of cafecitos and talked about Christmas.

"You guys just miss the whole point," argued Miguelito. "Your sermons are always the same — the shepherds, the Wise Guys, the Angels and Peace on Earth. But that's not Christmas. You say that the message of Christmas is Eternal. That means it's not just about 2000 years ago but it's today. Here! Now! Alive!"

And so, thanks to the wisdom of my imaginary friend, I will not share a story, as has been my tradition for twenty-seven years, but rather the Christmas mystery through Miguelito's eyes.

◄○►◄○►◄○►◄○►◄○►◄○►◄○►◄○►◄○►◄○►

The people who walked in darkness have seen a great light...

Christmas is Maryknoll Father Bob McCahill who shares a compound with fifty rickshaw drivers and devotes himself to simply being present to the Muslim communities of Bangladesh, serving others when permitted, praying for them always.

Upon those who dwelt in the land of gloom a light has shown.

Christmas is the cloistered Maryknoll Sisters in the Southern Sudan, praying for Peace among a people subject to starvation, exploitation, slavery and unspeakable injustice.

You have brought them abundant joy and great rejoicing as they rejoice before you as at the harvest.

Christmas is Roly and Tamara being in love and celebrating this holiday together — her first in a really real house all her own. It's Michael and Susan Lewis-Keister as husband and wife — filled with hope and promise, for each other and for all of us.

For the yoke that burdened them, the pole on the shoulder, the slavery to which they were subject, You, O Lord, have smashed.

Christmas is Jack Corey with his new liver. It is my friends in Recovery Michael and Ryan and Jimmy and Alan — alive, laughing and free. Christmas is the beginning of the commission "Go into the whole world and proclaim the Good News." It is Jack and Alan going tomorrow to New York to share their lives and stories — their addictions and resurrections — with Chinese priests and nuns and saying, "There is hope. God works in strange ways His wonders to perform. But God works great wonders."

For every boot that trampled in battle, every cloak rolled in blood will be burned as fuel for the flames.

Christmas is our constant prayer for Peace — for the safety not just of America's soldiers, sailors, airmen and Marines but for all men and women at all times and in all places.

For a child is born to us, a son is given to us.

Christmas is the Word of God made Flesh and dwelling amongst us. It is Billy and Jennie Mullowney saying that every day is Christmas because, when work is finished, he goes home, strips down to his skivvies and rolls around on the floor with their twins Will and Laurie.

They name him Wonder Counselor, God-Hero, Father-Forever, Prince of Peace.

We celebrate the words of the Angels "Peace on earth to all People of Good Will" when we pray for Father Roy Bourgeois, who in November led more than 10,000 protesters — many of them students from Jesuit high schools and colleges from California to Boston — to call for the closing of the U.S. Army School of the Americas at Fort Benning, Georgia, as they commemorated the 1989 murders of six Jesuit priests, their housekeeper and her daughter.

St. Paul wrote, "My beloved: The grace of God has appeared, saving all and training us to reject godless ways and worldly desires and to live temperately, justly, and devoutly in this age, as we await the blessed hope, the appearance of the glory of our great God…

Christmas is the indescribable celebrations tonight of Mike and Lisa Gorski and Leonard and Christine Traficanti. Having just returned from China, they mark the first Christmases of their daughters Carmelina Gorski and Vivian Xiao Traficanti and the realization of the words "When I was homeless you gave me shelter and love." And in years to come they will welcome Sophia Gorski and Olivia Lu Yin Traficanti

My beloved: Christ Jesus has given Himself for us… that we might be His People, eager to do what is good…

Christmas is our warmest memories of those who have gone to God, who by word and deed, through example and prayer have made us all that we are and have enabled us to become all that we yet hope to be.

Now it happened that, while they were there, the time came for her delivery, and she gave birth to her first born son and

wrapped him in swaddling clothes and laid him in a manger...

Christmas is Danny and Liz Munecas and their new daughter Ann Marie. It is Tico and Tata Munecas and their new life together. It is Mark Berube and his wife Stacy and their son Jake. It is our Hope and our hope that through the Mystery of the Incarnation and the Wonder of the Resurrection, in the providence of God, we are all one.

There were shepherds in that region living in the fields and keeping night watch over their flock.

Christmas is John and Nancy-Lee Thompson giving up his law practice in Coral Gables and their comfortable home here to move to Orlando so that he might assume the directorship of a program of prison ministry and proclaim the Good News to those who are outcasts.

Christmas is Jim Delph serving as a sponsor to a young African priest in Ocala and starting a new chapter of the Columbian Squires, the junior Knights of Columbus, almost forty years after we were involved in Squires in high school.

The angel of the Lord appeared to them and the Glory of the Lord shone round about them and they were filled with fear. The angel said to them, "Do not be afraid; for behold, I proclaim to you good news..."

Christmas is the beginning of miracles and the Season

of Endless Wonder. It is Dennis Heapy, who in July became the new Executive Director of Jesuit Volunteers International. Seventeen years ago, as a just-graduated alumnus of Boston University, he was working with the Jesuit Volunteer Corps in Belize, Central America. During a swimming lesson with kids with special needs, he was paralyzed at C3-4 — from his neck down. These are his words:

"A twist of fate, a miscalculation of the tides, and suddenly I was no longer the 'helper' but instead the person being helped. To be honest, I have always thought being Irish was my primary disability, but I am told by doctors that quadriplegia even beats being Irish. Since being disabled, I have learned that mutuality transcends labels, and that in relationships distinctions of helper and 'helpee' can disappear. This lesson was learned over the past seventeen years through my work in a variety of settings and with numerous populations. I have served as a teacher, chaplain, and counselor at high schools, colleges, hospitals, homes for elders, and homeless shelters.

"Two and a half years ago I was offered the opportunity to again do international work — this time in Nicaragua working on community access. Going back to Central America after an almost twenty-year hiatus was an eye-opening experience, to say the least. When I was in Belize, I saw the world through the eyes of a person who did not have a disability. I missed many things.

"My first trip back down to Central America as a person

with a disability was both exhilarating and life changing. Over the years I often wondered whether a person with my level disability could survive in a developing nation. My question was answered my first day in Nicaragua when coming down the street towards me was a person in a wheelchair with the same level disability as mine. Two thoughts ran through my mind. The first thought: 'What the heck happened to that guy and how does he survive?' My second thought was, 'Well, if he can do it, I can do it as well.'"

The Angel of the Lord said to them, "This will be a sign to you...."

Christmas is warm, rib-crushing, feelings of safety-giving hugs. It is loving parents nourishing and nurturing children; generous children caring for aging parents. It is friendships so deep that, when the words "I love you" are spoken, they are felt in the very core of our hearts.

Christmas is children's laughter, shared memories and anticipated adventures. It is hope and a sense of belonging – with people, among people, in people.

It is all that makes us most human because it is all that the Son of God embraced so lovingly when the Word became Flesh and dwelt amongst us.

It is prelude to the Eucharist. It is the Eucharist. It is Eucharist.

And suddenly there was with the angel a multitude of the heavenly host, praising God and saying, "Glory to God in the highest and on earth peace to those on whom his favor rests."

Christmas is Austin Gillen, a Notre Dame graduate (a fact that we will not hold against him) and John Schaus of St. John's College in Minnesota, Maryknoll Volunteers in Jilin China, who treated a young Chinese soldier and chemical warfare specialist with such open and unabashed kindness that, on the eve of their departure from China last Spring, he declared, "I am a soldier in the People's Army. A year ago, if my superiors had ordered me, I would have gone to war and killed Americans. Today, knowing you and calling you my friends, I must question war and the whole meaning and purpose of war."

Christmas is God's strangely wonderful, grace-filled and marvelous way His wonders to perform.

Or, at least that's what my imaginary friend Miguelito has taught me.

1998

Christmas Gifts Must Be P and L . . .

When I called the Gaine family a couple of weeks ago to invite them for this evening, Little Michael (he has informed me that that is his name — Little Michael) expressed his family's pleasure because coming here — to my family's home — for Christmas Eve Mass has become a family tradition.

There are Flynn Family Christmas traditions, too. All gifts must be wrapped. While Paul Klein, who is an adopted son, has his gifts wrapped by Neiman Marcus, my brother Michael does "designer wrapping." He doesn't "do the malls." He shops primarily at South Florida art festivals and small, out-of-the-way boutique shops.

Household appliances are household gifts — not personal, unless, of course, they're given to me.

Michael collects fish; Colleen collects expensive porcelains; Barry used to be easy because he has a Wild Turkey bourbon bottle collection but they've stopped making the special bottles. Now Barry is difficult because he has at least three and usually ten or twelve of everything and not knowing what to get him is traditional. When you were absolutely desperate, you could get theatre tickets for Mom and Dad or, if you're Michael, send them off to another luxury resort.

Otherwise, Dad was always delighted with the latest and most expensive golf equipment and Mommy, just in case you haven't noticed, collects Belleek, owls, and Hummels.

By tradition, cost is not important. On the lamp stand by her bed my mother still keeps a champagne glass with white silk orchids that I gave her one year; but, as a rule, all gifts must be P and L — permanent and lasting. When we were kids, Michael once bought a plastic cat-shaped planter that hung in the kitchen for more years than any of us can count. When it was finally "decorated out," he hung it in his garage. It's still there — P and L, Permanent and Lasting.

Probably the most spectacular of the P and L gifts was from Michael to Mommy at Christmas 1976. A white, flowering euphorbia. In its pot, it only stood yay high, a single spindly little stem with tiny white blossoms that looked like poinsettia the size of your cuticle. At the time, Michael was looking for the kind of job he wanted to make a career. Mom directed Daddy to plant her gift in the back yard, across the pool from the kitchen window. That way, every time she looked out the window she would see her "tree" and pray for Michael.

God was given an ultimatum — by the time the tree flowered the next year, somewhere around Thanksgiving, Michael was to have his dream job or God would be in serious trouble.

In February 1977, just a few weeks after the Michael Tree went into the ground, Miami was hit by a snowstorm. Yes. A snowstorm. The Michael Tree shriveled and appeared to die. The trunk, if you could call something as big around as your little finger a trunk, broke off at ground level. We were broken-hearted. Mom prayed. God trembled. In April, little shoots began to come up. In November 1977, they blossomed and Michael began his career with Xerox.

After Mass, go look. We trimmed the Michael Tree last March — down to knee high. Tonight, it is well over six feet. With a multitude of stems, it covers an area about twelve feet by eight feet. It blooms in all God's splendor.

<figure>◄○►◄○►◄○►◄○►◄○►◄○►◄○►◄○►◄○►◄○►◄○►</figure>

There's a chance that I'll get zapped for what I am about to say. So, some of you might want to move away just in case lightening comes through the window. But, the truth is that the Almighty doesn't always seem to be the best of caretakers.

Here's the story.

He created cherubim and seraphim, principalities and powers, all the choirs of angels. (That's a heck of a lot of angels.) Then he created archangels and put them in charge of the whole shooting match — angels, earth, the universe, which, by the way, in a real quirk of ironic brilliance, He decided to make ever-expanding. And there the problem began — four archangels (and one of them turned out to be a real trouble-maker) for the whole ever-expanding universe. Believe me, the division of labor wasn't quite fair: Raphael, we're still trying to figure out what he did; Gabriel — the Annunciation and that was it, he retired; Lucifer, boooo, hisssssss. And Michael. He not only had to put Lucifer in his place, but he was responsible for everything else, including border patrol on the ever-expanding universe.

One day after a pretty good chunk of eternity the Almighty noticed that Michael's wings were dragging. He looked like he had been through the wringer. (I was tempted to say "been through the winger," but even I wouldn't use a line like that.)

I understand that the Almighty is the Almighty but, as my mother would say, sometimes He just doesn't think because instead of assigning a few of Michael's jobs — like battling Lucifer — to Rafael or Gabriel, the Almighty decided that what Michael really needed was a walking stick. A walking stick? Where does an archangel walk? I suppose it was a big stick because I just suppose that archangels are pretty big guys.

Poor Michael. He had to care for the whole ever-expanding universe and carry the walking stick wherever he went because, as we all know, the Almighty is also All-Seeing. So, for literally eons the Archangel

Michael carried a walking stick wherever he flew. Then one day, as though he did not have enough to do, Michael was dispatched on a quick pre-Nativity site inspection. (It should be noted for history that Michael wasn't really too fond of the stable idea but when the Almighty gets something into His mind there's just no arguing with Him.) It was on this journey that Michael accidentally broke his walking stick. It wasn't really his fault. Without looking he stuck it in the crag of a rock and stepped and pulled at the same time. There was the ugly sound of wood cracking, and before he knew it, the archangelic walking stick was reduced to archangelic-sized splinters, which is to say, it had become several human-sized walking sticks.

There they stayed, splintered on the ground somewhere between Nazareth in Galilee and Bethlehem of Judea. Thus it was that one day a very tired man discovered just the stick he needed to lean on as he guided the tiny caravan of his wife and donkey. In truth, however, in its splintered condition it wasn't a very sturdy walking stick. And, despite the fact that it provided some appreciated support for part of the journey, it broke again, just a few miles outside of Bethlehem, leaving the man to manage the rocky roads on tired and unsure feet.

Day turned to night. The road was exchanged for a shack alongside the home of an inhospitable innkeeper.

In the poverty of a stable the traveler watched in awe the mystery of childbirth. A young mother's tears of pain became the laughter of joy. Emmanuel, God With Us! It was as the Almighty would have it — Wonder to shepherds, Hope for all, Joy beyond telling! Time passed. Messengers came. Danger threatened. A weary traveler bundled his wife and child. In the fading light of dusk, they fled those who would take the child's life. Distant stars brightened a desert sky. By moonlight, the refugees could see the approaching troops. Death on horseback drew ever closer. The road twisted and turned in the Judean countryside. Nowhere to hide.

The sound of horses' hooves echoed in the desert night. Nowhere to hide. Beyond the next hill, another turn. Then, where days before his walking stick had splintered, the traveler saw the brilliant white of a bush. Full. Lush. Towering. Limbs bent under the weight of God's majesty in beauty. Where everywhere there had been danger, where once there was no hope, now there was shelter and God's sure and certain embrace.

The child born in a stable was hidden, protected by blossoms of radiant white. Soldiers passed unknowing. Danger fled. So it was that Joseph and Mary went from Bethlehem of Judea to Nazareth and the Child grew in wisdom and age and grace before God and Man.

And Michael, the Archangel, watched in awe and understood that the Almighty is the Almighty.

After Mass, go out into the back yard and see our Michael Tree. Remember the words of the Almighty to his servant: "Be still and know that I am God." Contemplate the beauty of the Michael Tree brought from death to life, reborn, renewed, resurrected. And understand.

Now you know the stories of the Michael Tree.

$\mathscr{L}$ovely Lady, Dressed In Blue

There was a time - it seems now ages and ages past, — when, as a child, I learned:

Lovely Lady dressed in blue,
Teach me how to pray.
God was just your little boy;
Tell me what to say.
Did you lift him up sometimes
Gently on your knees?
Did you sing to him the way Mother does to me?
Did you hold his hand at night telling stories of the world —

Oh, and did he cry?
And do you think he cares if I tell him
things -
  Little things that happen. And do angels'
    wings make noise?
  Can he hear me if I speak low? Can he hear
me now?
  Tell me for you know.
  Lovely Lady dressed in blue,
  Teach me how to pray.
  God was just your little boy,
  And you know the way.

As I remember those lines, I wonder how he
learned.

Micah was tired. Very, very tired. He had already
been up since the first rays of dawn began to brighten
the eastern skies, outlining the hills of Judea and slowly
making clear the distance yet to be traveled. Shielded
from head to shoulders and shoulders to feet against
the intensifying sun and heat of the day by his course
shepherds' clothes, he had begun the day running well
ahead of his father and the others in the small caravan.

Now he found himself startled into wakefulness by a sudden jolt of the donkey-drawn cart into which he had stolen for refuge and rest when he became too exhausted by the day's journey to move any further on his own. For Micah, awakening in the donkey cart was frightening: His father, he thought, would be furious that he had not kept up with the others. Again, there would be shouts and harsh looks, threats of a beating if he could not do his part. His father would mock him before the other travelers and shake his fist in rage.

It seemed to Micah that his father was always angry. There was no longer any laughter, any gentleness, any caring in his father's face or voice. Threats, bitterness, anger. These had become the emotions of father's life in the months since Micah's mother died.

In the first days after her death — the neighbors said she was just too frail, too small to fight the fever that raged through so much of the town that month — Father sat sullen and quiet. He did not even speak to the boy who could neither understand nor tolerate his own grief.

Then, one morning Micah woke to find his father caught up in a flurry of activity. "We're going," the man announced, his voice booming through the darkness of the one room, almost windowless adobe home the family had shared through many happy times. Before he fully understood what was happening, Micah, at seven years old, found himself following his father down dusty streets and highways, leaving behind the only town and home he had ever known.

He did not remember the roads they traveled. There were rivers crossed, mountains climbed. Villages and towns. Maggido, Dor, and Accho, where they stayed — sometimes for a few days, sometimes for weeks. Jacob's Well and Mount Tabor, and finally, on the shore of the Sea at Sidon — in a foreign land, with foreign people — they settled, if it is possible for any man who is running from his own fears and angers to settle anywhere.

In Sidon Micah's father worked as a fisherman, often gone days at a time, frequently late into the night. The boy was left to himself, to see to his schooling, his own food, to care for himself. And, in a foreign land, among strangers, Micah found himself the object of their kindness.

The Gentile — foreign woman — next to whose home they lived would bring him hot meals when his father was away, often waiting as he ate, and when she had cleaned his plates, she would watch in silence until he fell asleep and quietly tucked him in before returning to her own home. There were never words exchanged — they did not speak the same language — except in her caring and concern.

*"Now it happened that at this time Caesar Augustus
issued a decree that a census of the whole world
should be taken. And everyone went to register,
each to his own town."*

So Micah and his father, Daniel bar Benjamin (Daniel, son of Benjamin) went from Sidon to Judea, to David's town of Bethlehem, because they were of the house and lineage of David.

Awakened by the jolting of the donkey cart, Micah looked out and saw the outlines of his town, the hills and streets he left so hurriedly only a few months – but in children's time ages and ages – ago. As the caravan drew nearer the town, his fears of his father's angry yelling grew less and less and the consciousness that he was "coming home at last" grew greater and greater.

Toward mid-afternoon on the outskirts of the town, the members of the caravan began to meld into the teeming mass of people who descended upon Bethlehem for the census. They had come from all parts of Judea and Galilee, each hoping to find housing with relatives or friends or in the limited number of places where travelers lodged.

Micah and his father made their way through the sunlit streets toward their own home, now so long abandoned. As his father trudged slowly before the cart, Micah jumped out and ran toward the doorsteps of the only home he had ever known. At last, he pushed open the door and stepped inside. Except for the heavy cover of dust, which had settled over everything, home was just as they had left it.

Behind Micah came his father.

In the following hours, Micah busied himself with stabling and feeding the donkey in the simple lean-to like structure attached to the side of his home. He unpacked the few simple utensils that had been brought in the cart and prepared the bed rolls. A meal was made of dried figs, grapes and a slab of cheese offered as a welcome by a neighbor. Then, at sunset, just as Micah was preparing to crawl into his bed roll, there came a knock at the door.

He watched as his father stood to answer and heard a stranger's voice:

"Please, sir. We have traveled all day in the heat and my wife is great with child. In the name of the Most High God, I beg you give us shelter."

In an instant, Micah felt the now all-too-familiar fear take hold of his body. His father's voice was booming, refusing the strangers shelter, threatening and sending them on their way. Micah could not understand — shelter was all they asked. There was no need for his father's anger.

He would tolerate this anger no longer. "It's not right," he heard himself saying. "They are strangers, just as we were. Wandering strangers in a strange land. They deserve to be treated as we have been, with kindness and care, even despite your anger. If you are too angry and selfish, too bitter to let them stay here, then I'll make room for them in the stable."

Pushing past his father, Micah grabbed an oil lamp from its stand by the door, and moving out into the night, took the stranger by his cloak sleeve, leading him to the stable. "It's not much," he apologized. "But I have just cleaned it, and there is hay; you can make a bed." Leaving the oil lamp with the two, Micah returned inside, surprised to find that, although he thought all the figs, grapes, and cheese had been eaten at dinner, there was still and ample amount on the table. Taking them up, he returned to offer them to his "guests."

Finally, Micah again crawled silently into his bedroll. His silence was not so much from anger at his father's continued rages as from the deep sense of hurt at his own inability to ease his father's pain and the suffering that this pain inflicted on others like the strangers, and if truth were known, upon himself.

Micah's sleep was fitful. Filled with dream-like memories of happier times, when his mother was alive and his father smiled and laughed. There were dreams of the endless days of travel after her death and nightmares of his father's rages. Late into the night he was awakened from these dreams by the sound of a baby's cry, and, rising from his cot, he made his way through the darkness of the home outside and to the stable.

There, to his wonder and amazement, on the pile of hay he had prepared only hours earlier, lay the woman cradling in her arms a newborn son. Micah watched in silence as the child slept. "But," he realized, "she is so uncomfortable there. She'll never be able to sleep if she must hold the baby." Quickly he looked around. He knew his father would never allow these strangers and their baby to sleep inside. But somewhere there must be a crib, a bed for the newborn child.

Then, he spied it — the manger from which he had fed the donkey only hours before. Micah cleaned it as best he could in the darkness of the night and filled the manger with fresh straw. But still, he thought, the straw itself is too coarse. It will stick through the swaddling clothes in which the child was wrapped and prick his skin.

There, in a crevice formed by the slant of the stable roof and the wall of his home, where it had hung for as long as he could remember, Micah saw a small plant. His mother, he recalled, had nursed it for years with gentle care always telling him that one day it would bloom and fill that small corner of the stable with its beauty. But nothing ever happened and Micah had always regretted that she would never see the blooms for which she had waited and worked so long.

"The leaves," he thought. "The leaves will make a perfect cover for the hay."

Taking the plant down from its perch he stripped away the leaves to lay them on the hay. And the Babe's mother "laid him in the manger because there was no room for them in the place where travelers lodged."

In the countryside close by there were shepherds keeping watch in turn over their flocks and when the angel of the Lord appeared to them and announced to them the birth of this child, they came in haste and found Mary and Joseph and the baby lying in the manger.

Through the night, shepherds came, telling strange stories of how they had come to know of this wondrous child through angels that appeared to them as they watched over their flocks. In the end, it was all too much for Micah, who fell asleep there on the edge of the hay pile, waking only at the first light of dawn. Even as he realized where he was and remembered all that had occurred during the night, he knew that something mysterious had happened. Something was different.

Then he saw it — his mother's precious plant just as he had left it hours before, naked, leafless and yet magnificently in bloom. Micah was awe struck so great was his surprise.

Slowly, he began to look around. The shepherds

had gone; dawn, breaking quietly, revealed the sleeping figures of husband and wife. In the manger, atop the leaf-covered straw, wrapped in swaddling clothes, the Babe — his eyes fixed on the magnificent wondrous blooms.

Micah drew close and began to speak: "All babies should sleep in mangers," he said, "So that when they wake they can see the beauty of God's creation...

"Welcome, baby, to this world. And let me tell you what you might learn. Share everything. Play fair. Spit on your bait — if you want to catch fish. Don't hit people. Put things back where you find them. Clean up your own mess. Don't take things that aren't yours. Say you are sorry when you hurt someone. Wash your hands before you eat.

"Take a nap every afternoon. When you go out into the world, hold hands and stick together. Pour honey on fried chicken. Be aware of Wonder.

"Don't be afraid of your feelings. It's alright to be angry, as long as you don't hurt anyone.

"Mix black bean soup with white rice and be sure to try paella. Remember to be kind to strangers because you were born a stranger and someone was kind to you. Say 'I'm sorry' and be willing to forgive. Always be patient because sometimes you'll want others to be patient with you.

"Teddy bears are for hugging and making us feel safe, and Teddy Bear picnics are on Saturday afternoons.

Every child should have a Teddy Bear.

"Milk and cookies are for sharing," Micah continued. "Mommies bake cakes on Tuesdays and Wednesday is Prince Spaghetti Day. Hug your friends, and don't ever refuse a hug to someone who needs one. Hugs are why God gave us arms. Give to others freely. That's what God asks of us, and if we do, God will give freely to us. See what he has done to my mother's plant that gave its leaves for your bed.

Micah did not hear his father enter the stable. Daniel stood silent, seen only by the woman who watched the stranger-host speak softly to her infant son. Two parents listened and, perhaps, they learned.

"Remember, sometimes when daddies are silent or yell and get angry, it's because they are frightened and scared or lonely and hurt."

"Make peace, and be aware of Wonder."

Micah's father listened.

"And Mary guarded all these things in her heart."

The Heritage

The night air had slowly turned perceptibly colder.

And with its new-felt chill came a subtle, quiet stillness. Time for Ruben to put aside the angers and bitterness of the day. Satisfied by his evening meal of goat's milk cheese, bread, and a small scrap of lamb, tired by the toils of the day, Ruben felt strangely comfortable in the heavily laden, musty atmosphere that had become his home.

It should not have been. It should not have been home. It should not have been comfortable. It wasn't right. Inside him boiled the steaming combination of anger, loss and frustration — a cauldron of emotions quieted only by the peace of sleep.

"Home," he thought. "Home. Not at all. Not home. Nothing. No place really. Just a spot, a place to try to sleep." Abandoned, almost windswept by the breeze that seeped in through the splintered boards or under the door.

"To think," he told himself, " this had once been mine. Now, now... Perhaps, just maybe... I am its.

"No..." He would stop the thoughts. To yield to them now would be to yield to his anger, and that would just make sleep all the more difficult and the cold all the more painful. Better to sleep, at least then he would not feel the cold. "Better to sleep," he told himself and made his way to a point protected from the wind, away from the doors and blocked by a small partition.

No... Not yet.

Rousing himself, breaking away from the cold-induced sleep that had almost claimed him, Ruben recalled that there remained one task yet to be completed. One he had, in the desperation of his hunger, forgotten.

There had been no money to buy a new Menorah. That was alright. Despite all that had been taken away from him – the land, the house, even the inheritance to which he was entitled as the firstborn (and only) of the family, he had, when all was said and done, managed to preserve two things: a sense of the Tradition of his ancestors he received from his parents, for he was, after all, a child of the Covenant, and the Menorah.

When the word came with all its bitter implications that his parents had been killed, he knew in his grief that the greed of others would be his own undoing. There would be no inheritance. He would have no rights. To join the ranks of the outcasts – the widows and the orphans – that would be his lot.

And so, even before he would yield to his grief, before he would shed a tear, he stole into his own home, quickly grabbing up his cloak. It had been spun from the wool of his father's sheep by his mother's own hands. Dyed with care and pride, she formed the yarn into a cloak that, originally, had weighed almost as much as himself when his mother presented it to him on the first of the Eight Nights. It was his. From his father's sheep and his mother's hands. No one would take it away from him. Then, looking around, he spotted it. Carefully wrapped. Protected by generations and tradition. The Menorah saw the daylight — and the night — only on the most special of occasions.

It had been fashioned by his great, great, great, grandfather, a veteran of the three-year struggle between the Maccabees and the Syrian Greeks 165 years earlier. His ancestor had forged the candle stick to commemorate "God's great goodness to us" as each generation of first-born sons had shared the tradition with the next.

When the enemies had been routed and the Temple cleansed, the Sons of the Covenant sought to honor the Lord of History by lighting a fresh oil lamp in the Sanctuary. Miraculously, as a sign of His love and a promise of His presence, the single day's oil continued to burn — not for one but for eight days. And so, each year and from generation to generation, beginning with the ancestral veteran of that struggle, the family of Ruben celebrated the miracle by lighting candles, one for each day that the Temple oil lamp had burned.

A child of the Covenant and a son and heir of tradition, Ruben secreted away his dual inheritance, and, only when his cloak and Menorah were safe did he yield to his grief.

Now, years later, rousing himself from the edge of sleep, he gathered his cloak about him and drew the Menorah from its hiding place behind the stall where the oxen slept. With care, he placed it on the shelf above his sleeping place and in the central position he placed the first of the candles – the "shammus" or leader" from which, through the course of the coming nights, all the others would receive their lights and two other candles to mark the first and now the second nights.

Grabbing up a small handful of straw he obtained a light from the lamp which hung just inside the door, and with the pride that comes from participating in an on-going tradition, he lit the shammus. From it, he kindled the first two of the eight candles.

Faithfulness having been observed, he wrapped himself again in his cloak and slid quietly to sleep beneath the shelf on which he had placed his precious Menorah.

In the late hours of the night, however, Ruben's quiet, unangered sleep was almost gently disturbed. Shaken, roused first by the increasing intensity of the cold, and then by the soft yet pain-filled sounds – voices breaking into his dreams, interrupting his sleep.

The voice was deep, husky, pained and uncomfortable. "We saw your shammus... I'm sorry."

In the dim light, Ruben could see the lines of exhaustion etched deeply in the man's face. He was tired... clearly a stranger in a strange land.

"I...," the man continued. "We thought... you see, my wife... She...."

Suddenly the quiet of his voice was overpowered by a pain-filled yell. A woman's yell, more a scream, pain-filled – agonizing.

As Ruben pulled himself back to consciousness, the man disappeared in the direction of the woman's screams. Within seconds Ruben was beside him. The woman smiled quietly – weak and tired in the throes of childbirth.

"It's the census... we came... my wife, our first child... It's time...." The man could hardly put words together. But Ruben understood. They had come to his town, to the City of David. The man and his wife to register for a census that the Roman Emperor had decreed. They had traveled far. They must be hungry. Certainly, she was in pain.

Ruben understood.

They were outcasts. No room for them in a city crowded with others who had come for the same reason. No room for outcasts – just as there was no longer any room for him.

Ruben raced.

To find more light. To get help. To make the outcast stranger... To make them what? To make them at home? Here, beneath the shammus. In the light of tradition.

"And she gave birth to her first born son and...."

A baby. Small. Wrinkled. All red and pink. Squirming and crying. Shivering in the cold.

"And she gave birth to her first born son and wrapped him in swaddling clothes and laid him in a manger...."

"I'm sorry," said Ruben. "I'm sorry for the smells. I guess since my parents died I've gotten used to living here. I'm sorry for the cold and the wind. The stable walls have rotted pretty badly without my father to take care of them. The wind comes through. But I've tried to block the space under the doors...

"I wish...."

Ruben's mind flooded with thoughts. In all those days and years since... No family. No one to... He was lonely and suddenly the loneliness was broken. Shattered. He had a family... They shared, they changed his hovel... it was home. In the light of the shammus. In the light of tradition.

"I'm sorry," Ruben stammered again. "I wish...," he began as his eyes caught sight again of the now flickering "leader" candle. "I wish I had a brother...." The words came out before he could catch them. "I'm sorry." Again he stammered. "I wish there was more I could do. That's what I meant to say."

Again, the shammus candle flickered. Dawn would be breaking soon. It had become truly cold. The woman and the child both shivered in the dew-filled, pre-dawn chill.

"And she brought forth her first born son and wrapped him in swaddling clothes and laid him in a manger because there was no room for them in the place where travelers lodged."

"But I do. I wish I had a brother," Ruben said. He almost began to cry, remembering his own family. His father, so much like this man, deep-voiced and quiet spoken, rough hard hands with a gentleness.

His mother...truly good, loving...after all hadn't she worked so long and hard to spin the wool, to prepare.... My cloak.

"And she brought forth her first born son and wrapped him in swaddling clothes and laid him in a manger because there was no room for them in the place where travelers lodged."

"My cloak," said Ruben. And in an instant it was off his shoulders and over his head. Folded and placed on the manger straw. Carefully folded with a large pocket atop, just right to hold and warm a new-born child wrapped in swaddling clothes. "My mother made it for me. She spun the wool and dyed it and everything for me." Ruben's thoughts and feelings raced and he began to swell with the pride and warmth of all that the moment carried for him.

"She made it for me... and for my brother," he said.

"He is," the woman answered. "He is.... Your brother.

All of this in the light of the shammus. In the light of Tradition.

"Sleep well, brother," said Ruben.

$\mathcal{L}$et's Go to Christmas

The young priest (Well, perhaps it's no longer appropriate to call him "young." After all, the years have begun to take their toll and there are tell-tale streaks of gray in his hair. But it is the holiday season and we can be kind.)

The young priest straightened himself slowly from his deep bow, a smile broadening on his face with each new inch of stature as he righted himself. He had just finished the joyous liturgical Proclamation of Christmas: "Today...in the five thousand, one hundred and ninety-ninth year of the creation of the world, from the time when God in the beginning created the heavens and the earth...in the sixth age of the world, when the whole world was at peace, Jesus Christ, the eternal God and Son of the Eternal Father... was born in Bethlehem of Judah of the Virgin Mary...."

Turning toward the congregation, he could feel the anticipation building within him. He had been waiting — inhibited by his own concern about the reaction of others — for months now. Waiting precisely for this moment. "Merry Christmas. Peace be with you." The words almost burst out. They had been boiling inside of him, born in a unique, special late night session with Ken.

As Father Paul moved now to the presidential chair and seated himself for the first readings of the Liturgy, he thought back over those many special encounters with Ken. The old man was the quintessential Florida retiree — in his pastel-colored blue shirt with the blue polyester pants and the white patent leather shoes and belt.

His Nebraska farm had been fully mechanized. His oldest son, Jack, a graduate of the School of Agriculture of the University of Nebraska, had assumed control of the day-to-day operations of the family-owned acreage. The second son, Jim, had long since begun to apply his degree in business administration to the financial planning of the entire enterprise. And Ken, widowed "oh, for a long time now," often felt left out at the family dinner table when conversation about his farm was in terms that he could not understand.

The time had finally come when the winters there were "just too much." They made a family vacation out of it — Ken, sons, daughters-in-law and three grandchildren (the dogs stayed at home) — and flew to Miami. It had been a real vacation, too: Disney World, Seaquarium, snorkling in the Keys, but a vacation with a purpose. Time was set aside to find a winter home for Ken. Ultimately, it was determined that he would buy a comfortable, new mobile home on the western fringes of Miami.

Ken had mixed feelings. He knew that Nebraska's winters were out for him. But, of course, he would be going back there for summers. It was a strange place, Miami. Most of the people in the trailer park were older and no one seemed to speak English. There was, however, a big field next to the park and two old Cuban gentlemen had cut out a pretty good-sized year-round garden for themselves. Best of all, despite their extremely limited English, they made it abundantly clear that Ken would be *"en su casa"* — at home — with them in their *"nuestra"* — our — garden.

The final selling point had been that a brand new Catholic church was opening in just a few weeks on the other side of the trailer park.

So it was that one Saturday evening in late November, just at that time in the year when the local news reporters were beginning to talk a lot about "big snow storms" up north, Ken appeared for the Saturday Vigil Mass. His coming was announced by a cloud of smoke that bellowed up from his pipe and surrounded the old man's head. Father Paul had to step back for a second just to catch a breath of fresh air. "Merry Christmas, Father. My name is Ken Eastmen."

More than slightly startled by the unusual greeting, Paul was still searching for a response when Ken continued. "Father," he fairly shouted in a stage whisper that could surely be heard in the last row of any giant theatre. "Father, could I go to confession?" And before Paul could respond or call him to the privacy of the sacristy, the old man had begun. Fortunately, the church was still almost empty, and besides, the old man really did not have much of interest to confess — mostly just a lot of missed prayers.

Following the evening Mass, Ken was waiting for Paul. There were questions — weekday and weekend mass schedules and parish activities — and there was history — how he had moved to Nebraska at four years of age with his recently widowed mother "that was in 19 and ought something." How he had finished sixth grade when he began working on a farm. Marriage, a world war, children, his own farm, retirement... It all came out in that booming whisper from behind an impenetrable cloud of pipe smoke.

Finally, a question: "Father, do you like fresh vegetables? Not as good as we grown them in Nebraska, mind you...not very good soil.. But those old Cuban men do a pretty good job and we get a lot more than we can use among us."

And so it began. Each Saturday evening, for as long as there would be snow on the ground in Nebraska, Father Paul would be greeted with "Merry Christmas" and a bag of fresh vegetables and another confession of missed prayers.

It had gone that way for a number of years - snow up North, followed by "Merry Christmas," fresh vegetables and missed prayers – when one Saturday evening it was not Ken but an elderly Cuban woman who arrived. Ken, she explained, was sick and, could Father, whenever he had the time of course, come and hear his confession and bring him communion.

That evening, following a wedding, Father Paul braved his fear of the cloud of smoke which he knew would be bubbling up from Ken's ever present pipe and knocked on the door of the trailer. Greeted by the Cuban woman, who concerned herself with bustling around with *caldo* – soup – and chicken and just plain being busy, he settled himself next to Ken's bed for what would become a most delightful visit. In the end, however, he found himself, even as he prepared to leave because of the late hour, or perhaps it was in spite of the late hour, unable to contain himself.

"Ken," he asked, "I've really got to know. Why is it, good sir, that every time I see you at church, here tonight, in the shopping center, every time, you say 'Merry Christmas?'"

Ken's eyes fairly danced.

"Oh, Father, that goes back a long time ago. So very long ago. I'm not even sure you want to know or that you have the time," he protested. But Paul had already settled himself back into the bedside chair, as if to assure Ken just how deeply he desired an answer, and so the old man continued.

"There was one Christmas... back there outside Omaha... my mother had been working for a long time already. She used to do anything to make sure that we had the best meals and pretty good, not exactly the best, but pretty good clothes. I guess, now, as I remember, she must have been working a couple of different jobs. But that Christmas there just wasn't any money...

"And so, on Christmas Eve... oh, the snow was so deep and it just kept snowing.

"It wouldn't let up. There was no way of going to church... We had a fire in the fireplace. I had cut a lot of wood during the week and there was a big pile of it in the living room. Mother, my brother and I... We started to sing Christmas carols... my brother and I weren't very good, we hadn't really learned a lot of the words and I guess we just pretended.

"Mother apologized for not being able to give us any gifts... No gloves, no sweaters, and no toys.

"So she made a special 'gift' for us.

"She told us to close our eyes and imagine.

"To imagine... and she would give us Christmas.

"Go on, Father. You can... Let me 'give you Christmas.'"

Before he understood what was happening, Paul was a part of the story. His eyes closed. He was allowing himself to be given Christmas.

"Imagine the stable, Father... Imagine outside. The cold... Dew on the ground, silver under the moon light. It catches on the cuffs of your pants, wet and cold, and soaks your shoes. You can imagine it.

"Inside - dark, the air so heavy...

"The smell.... Oh, I remember the smell even now... The cows, lambs, the donkey. It had been a tough trip for him. The fire, so small... low, built right down on the ground of sticks and twigs. Not much of a fire, really. But, if you sit, if you really huddle up close, it helps... Not a whole lot, but it helps to get you warm. It doesn't give much light, but you can see by it... just barely.

"A couple of shepherds... Oh, how worn and wrinkled they look. Centuries of wind and weather mark their faces. I wonder if they've ever felt soft.

"Oh, at first I thought he was one of the shepherds, too, cloaked in that lambs' wool fur... It's Joseph. I guess you can say he looks like Everyman. He's not old, but he's not young either, is he?

"Oh, Lord... She's so small... So frail... So tired... That poor woman... Birth relief written all over her face. It's not... I'm not sure what it is that her face says. She's there, you can barely see the whole face, covered by her shawl. No, now... Now you can see it... She's... beautiful. Not pretty, but beautiful.

"My Lord, she's the Mother of God...

"And there...

"SO SMALL.

"She holds him, and I am there. I can see it all.

"Watch with me.

"Stand with me.

"Oh, Lord...

"She sees... She sees me.

"She smiles.

"She calls. She calls me. Not with her voice. Her eyes. She calls me.

"And... I... step... closer...

"'Here,' she says 'Here...

"Her arms reach out... 'Here, take Him. It's alright. He would want it this way. Here. Take Him in your arms...

"And He is there... He is here. MY GOD."

An instant eternity, or perhaps eternity in a brief instant, passed. Father Paul lost all sense of time until

Ken spoke again.

"It's time, now, Father. We must give him back. It's hard. So hard. Her arms are out now. I know... she looks so small, so frail, so beautiful, so WEAK... But she's carried him all this time. She can carry him now... again. Let's go, Father. One last look.

"It's okay. We can come back. You can come back tomorrow. Let's go, Father."

The visit – no. Not the visit but the visits were over.

"You see, Father," said Ken. "My mother gave us a very special gift that night. She gave us Christmas. And I can go there every day. And, Father, now so can you. You see, Father, that's why I say 'Merry Christmas.' Because I go there every day."

Suddenly, before he had realized it, the first readings of the Liturgy of the Word had been completed. Father Paul called himself out of his own thoughts. It was his turn. As he moved toward the pulpit, he prayed for Ken, who had not come back this year. He prayed for himself, that one day, in May or July or August, he might have the courage, not just to "go there" – for now he went there all the time – but the courage to say "Merry Christmas."

"In those days," he began, "Caesar Augustus published a decree... And suddenly there was with the angel a whole multitude of the heavenly host, praising God and saying, 'Glory to God in high heaven, and peace on earth to those on whom his favor rests.' And this," proclaimed Paul, raising high over his head the Book of the Gospels, "is the Good News of our salvation."

Stepping to the center of the main aisle, he began his sermon. "Merry Christmas, my friends. Come with me to Christmas. Come with me and let me give you Christmas...."

A Tale of Francis and Claire, Danny and Lisa

I've often wondered how some of my personal heroes might celebrate Christmas, if they were alive today.

This brief effort is my flight into fantasy with the persons of St. Francis of Assisi, who according to tradition, gave us the first Christmas crib, and St. Claire. And, yes. I know that Francis was never ordained a priest; he was a deacon. But this is my fantasy.

There was something remarkably out of place about both of them. At first blush they looked (How to describe it?) "out of place in the modern world." And the more one focused on the two plodding figures outlined by a horizon of waiving fields of sugar cane, crystalline blue skies and puffy cumulus clouds, the more one stared at the strange moving figures carved in flesh and cloth, the more one waited patiently to understand precisely what it was that gave them their unique air of strangeness, then the more one realized that it was not so much they themselves. (Although they would certainly have captured the careful observer's imagination and attention in and of themselves.) It was something else. Something non-human that made the two figures even the more remarkably human.

To say that the "something" was "too big" would have been almost a lie. They were huge. "Out of style" was not even socially polite – it would have been a complete and utter distortion. They were ugly – the huge brogan-style boots. Black "clod hoppers" that, with their weight and too practical appearance, caused the men who wore them to look even more distinct, capturing a strange mixture of curiosity and sympathy.

Their two-man procession had, by now, been marching against the back drop of fading afternoons for several months. Each day – each afternoon – the same. From far out in the fields, when others had quit the cane and corn and chosen to ride back on the tractors and flat beds of their labor, they would begin. Never a word spoken; their own private worlds separated by perhaps fifty or one hundred and fifty feet. They followed, in an almost ritualistic fashion, the same daily journey. From the fields, along the shoulders of the highway. Silent. Stopping only once while the lead acolyte dropped quietly from sight for a moment, hidden behind the swinging doors of a dilapidated roadside station that served both gas and beer, only to emerge again carrying his two large quart bottles – both wrapped in brown paper bags – of Budweiser.

The procession would then move to its penultimate station – a small park and picnic area aside an almost picturesque pond. There, straddling a bench next to a crumbling old table, the taller, larger man would open one of his bottles and slowly, almost methodically, begin to drink in absolute silence.

The other, somehow not wishing to invade the privacy of the moment, would settle himself into the grass. And from the recesses of faded overall pockets he would produce a roll or two, or perhaps several slices of bread now balled tightly together. Even before he could begin to scatter the crumbs, he would find himself the target of the area's birds. Honking, squawking, pushing and shoving at each other in an attempt to share in the meal of dough, they seemed to respond to the silent man with the ugly brogans and the torn work shirt by instinct and with familiarity and a sense of confidence.

If the truth were known, the two men were strangers. Their procession, as much the product of happenstance now turned habit, as anything else.

This simple liturgy would end here. Silence marked only by the sounds of nature and the fading of day into twilight. There was never a word spoken, no contact ever made between the two. Just a quiet passing of time that ended with their disappearance into the night. And so, it was particularly noteworthy that on this evening the bird feeder rose even before the sunset had begun to turn purple and moved toward the beer drinker. Hand extended and in a voice almost lyrical with an accent that defied description, he began, "I'm Giovanni Bertandone and I... I just wish to ask you, to invite you... would you join us for dinner... It's not much. Just we...we would... You see. She's... Come. I'll show you the way...."

The poor beer drinker was mystified, speechless. Giovanni had, somehow, gained hold of his hand and was refusing to let go. There would be no saying "no." He found himself being pulled upright and along. Barely able to reach back and grab the second bottle that only an instant earlier had been at his feet. "I... I...," he protested.

"Not to worry. Come. It will be alright...."

Now the second acolyte had taken the lead and there would be no stopping him. He would have his way. However gently, he would have his way.

"But my wife...."

And gentle resoluteness suddenly yields to shining joy in the face of the determined guide. "All the better. We'll stop for her and the two of you will be our guests... Claire will be so pleased. I don't know what she has prepared... It is always a surprise." His accent was lyrical, mystical, assuring even in the haltedness of his speech. "She's working at the Women's Center, teaching the Haitians and the Salvadorans... I'll never understand where she gets her language skills... But she manages... and so do they. Somehow, she's never been afraid to beg for what she needs, even from the first, and she has never been without... She's made my life miserable these last few days, worried that there would not be a guest for the table tonight. I shall forever be grateful to you... To the two of you.

"Come. She'll be waiting. Let's gather your wife...."

The poor farmhand was thunderstruck. He who had so jealously guarded his isolation now found that not only had his isolation been shattered, but he was being drawn into something that he could neither understand nor resist.

"My name is Giovanni but everyone calls me Francis. My father was a merchant who thought that all things French were good and he wanted me to do business with the French... He determined that they were the key to business. Can you imagine that he even called me Francisco — the Frenchman? What a name for an Italian!"

The processional lead changed again, and even while Giovanni/Francis continued his musical monologue, the two made their way to a tumbling down, broken-porched migrant worker home. Francis stepped back and waited while his newly met associate climbed the steps and disappeared behind a slamming screed door. With time the man emerged again, sheltering in the cradle of his arm a small slip of a woman, who herself was cradling a well-bundled infant.

Now Francis took the lead, virtually singing an aria

as he continued. He never even asked their names. It seemed as if he had known the two, no, the three forever. There was no need for names. They were important just because they were themselves and they were to be his guests this night.

The extended procession came to a halt before a second migrant shack, almost the duplicate of the first. In an instant Francis had the door open and was shepherding his guests inside.

"Claire, Claire... we have company."

She was a small, slight, magnificently beautiful woman twelve years younger than him. In an instant, chairs were produced from the recesses of a stark, simple residence marked only by a table, oven, and small cot. When Danny and Lisa, as they introduced themselves, had been settled in, Francis with a flourish produced a bottle of white wine from a cabinet beneath the sink.

"For a special occasion, for friends, for Christmas," he said as he proceeded to serve the sparkling liquid in unmatched coffee cups and glasses.

The two guests sat. He staring, still unable to understand the dramatic movement of the previous thirty or forty minutes that had brought him to this point. She overwhelmed, shy, afraid.

Claire now slipped back to the oven and began to prepare the last stages of the evening meal. Gently she signaled to the woman. Come. Gathering towels from a small closet and the pillow from the cot, Claire made a small crib for the child, and in the semi-privacy of the kitchen, the two women began to talk.

Within minutes the young girl's story was pouring out and Claire's quiet gentleness allowed it all. Her name was Lisa and she was desperately in love with Danny. He was a good man who tried hard but the last several years had been just too much for him. He had had his own business — success after years of struggling against a painful family background and a myriad of problems. They had fallen in love and stayed that way from the first time they met.

Then his mother became sick — cancer. Danny had a hard time dealing with it. He couldn't sleep at night and when he did the dreams were so terrible. At first the doctor just gave him some sleeping pills, and then there were others — for his nerves during the day, then to get him going in the morning. One thing led to another and he was a drug addict.

And not just that but there was cocaine and then the money started to go and the jewelry, the car, the house, the business. He was hooked, and hurt, and sick. Finally, he ended up in jail.

More than anything he hated himself for what he had done to his wife and family. Jail was hard, but it saved Danny's life from the drugs that were killing him. Yet, it left him so afraid. Afraid of the real world, afraid of getting back in trouble, afraid he couldn't stay clean.

His last prison camp had been here in this almost-middle-of-the-Everglades town. She had come to see him every other weekend. And on the day of his release, she had been there for him. But Danny was still so scared that, with the $100 in his pocket that the State had given him, he settled here. In this migrant camp, a few miles from the prison gate.

Here he works the fields each day. There's barely enough to survive on, but there's no drugs and there is no pressure. Yet he feels so depressed. He comes home in silence at night with a bottle of beer that he drinks with dinner. And later he sits in the dark and cries. He even says that there is no God, or if there is, He's either deaf or has forgotten Danny.

Her days are simple. She delivered the baby, Jeremy, two weeks after Danny's release. And the boy, just three months old, demands all of her time. Days are rough but just to be with Danny and the baby... Nights are good.

Now, eyes suddenly downcast, she drops her voice almost to a whisper, conscious that just the other side of the room her husband could not help but hear her.

For his part, Francis made himself comfortable in a most uncomfortable chair and earnestly attempted to draw Danny into conversation. And, when all his efforts met with silence, Francis took up a monologue of his own — about the days, the beauty of the fields, the migrant men and women who toil there, their goodness, the stars and the night sky. On and on in almost a celebration of beauty.

Sensing the young girl's unease, Claire took up the conversation, while, at the same time, beginning to serve a meal of roast chicken, vegetables, and even homemade rolls. They had come here together. They had been friends "oh, it seems like forever" — she and Francis. She lived in the Women's Community Center, teaching mostly household and parenting skills. Perhaps, Lisa might want to come and spend an afternoon; there's even a play room for the baby.

Mostly, she continued, Francis worked the fields and talked to the people and stayed alone here. He had come because he heard they needed someone, someone who spoke broken English and equally broken Spanish and French. (Oh, how he loved to speak French and to sing the old French songs, even though his native language is Italian, Claire added. Despite all of the protests about his father naming an Italian boy "the Frenchman.")

Now it was Francis who was becoming visibly uncomfortable. Claire could sense it even before he began to interrupt her with a laughing, "Come, come, ladies. To table, ladies. To table."

The wine glasses filled, the plates laden, the four moved to the table, and, before either Danny or Lisa realized what had happened, they found their hands grasped tightly by the hosts who sat on either side of them. "Bless us, Gentle Lord, and these your gifts which we receive from your bounty through Christ our Lord, whose birth we celebrate this night."

It was a strange meal, eaten in almost complete silence. But somehow the presence of the four — their gift to each other — made the room alive. Light. Happy. Claire excused herself only once, to return with freshly filled plates for both the men, and "just a little more" for herself and her other guest.

Then, just as the two men had begun to settle into their post-meal haze, Claire spoke: "Francis, it's time."

One might have said it was the wine. Some might have blamed the quickness with which they were up from the table, the child bundled, the four, no, the five out on the street and transported deep into the migrant camp on magic. But suddenly there they were — before a small, wooden church, its bell clanging hollowly into the night, its porch filled with people — brown, black and white, speaking English, Spanish and Creole.

Danny tried to protest, but was quickly silenced by Francis begging a moment's leave and Claire's gentle voice explaining, "This is really why Francis is here. Somehow they need him."

Claire led them up the steps and through the open double doors. Inside… a quiet anticipation. It seemed as if the whole world was waiting on tip toes. Candles on the altar, the strange semi-darkness of a church that could only be lit by bare bulbs hung from wires in an equally bare ceiling.

Suddenly, seemingly from nowhere, between husband and wife, stepped Francis. Coming up behind them, his arms spread wide and catching them up in his own step, he pulled them toward the foot of the aisle. Then a step ahead and he whirled, and for the first time inside the church, they saw him. A heavy-set robe of brown, covered by a white gown that hung almost to the floor, atop it all a stole of every color coming down in front and over each shoulder and hidden below a cowl collar that hung half-way to the back.

Beneath it all the brogans.

"The child, please...," Francis whispered, as catching the baby into his own arms and sweeping them up in the expanse of his vestments, he erupted into song – a song that spread quickly through the congregation blending perfectly in Spanish and English and Creole: "Hark, the herald angels sing...Glory to the New Born King."

At the sanctuary, Francis stopped and gently placed the still sleeping child in – wonder of wonders – a manger, filled with fresh straw and topped by the multi-colored blanket of a Central American native.

Danny and Lisa were stunned. How to respond?

They stood for a moment, and Francis, now facing the congregation, began to declare: "The birth of Our

Lord, Jesus Christ....."

From the side of the sanctuary an altar boy appeared. Holy water bucket in hand, he moved toward Francis, who began sprinkling first the sleeping child in the manger and then the congregation.

Claire pulled Danny and Lisa into the front pew alongside herself and in a rapid fire whisper began: "We, I mean... I thought you knew. Sometimes Francis just doesn't explain. He came here a year ago as a priest to serve..."

By now, with a radiant solemnity, Francis had begun the Mass.

A reading, a song joyously entered into by the entire congregation, another reading, and then Francis stood and began: "In those days, a decree went forth from Caesar Augustus ordering that a census of the whole world be taken... And Mary treasured all of these things in her heart."

The Gospel completed, Francis moved to the front of the aisle. And, slowly bowing, kissed the forehead of the sleeping manger child. Straightening himself, he turned, looked toward the congregation and into the heart of Danny and said softly, "Be still... Be still and know that God is God."

$\mathcal{A}$ngry, Furious, Boiling

$\mathbf{I}$t was already nine-thirty on Christmas Eve and Karl was… (I'm not sure just what the word is… more than "upset." "Angry" doesn't quite make it. "Furious" is probably too strong).

Karl was boiling. That's it. Karl was boiling.

The feeling started on the Monday evening of the week before Christmas when he was assigned as "the priest" to hear confessions. Much as a boil starts slowly in a really large kettle, it continued to develop through the course of the week as, each night, he was "the priest," while the pastor watched *Jeopardy*.

It wasn't that he resented the confessions. He was, sometimes, glad that it was he to whom the folks were coming — rather than the pastor, who he knew would have been less than understanding and far too punitive and judgmental. They were hurting people. Two different teenage girls who had had abortions and were overcome with the consequent emotions; parents worried about children grown alienated from the Church and how should they handle it when the kids came home for the holiday and Mom and Dad wanted to know what to do about Christmas Mass; abused wives; the adult children of alcoholic parents; those who had not been to the sacraments for forty-two, or eighteen, or fifty-one years because of shame or pride or having been hurt by the last priest they approached; and, of course, the "little old ladies in tennis shoes" whose last confessions were three weeks ago or Sunday or "this morning" and whose biggest sin was "I lost patience."

"Yes," Karl would think, "MINE."

He really enjoyed celebrating the Sacrament, even though it was like alternately being pounded by the Miami Hurricanes' defensive line when the really heavies came along and being stoned to death with marshmallows when the little old lady "scrups" (priest talk for "scrupulous") whispered about their impure thoughts while watching Donahue or Oprah.

But it was the idea that he had been "assigned" as

"the priest," while the pastor guessed at questions. And, even worse, it was the horror of waiting for — the anticipation of — the pastor's interminable sermon tonight at the Midnight Mass that had really gotten his stomach churning.

Karl knew the sermon almost word-for-word. He had heard it each of his past eight years assigned to the parish, rattled off in a monotone Irish brogue with too frequent references to the "tree persons in One God," and the "Tree Wise Men" and the "tree little shepherd boys." (How he ever came up with the "tree shepherd boys" Karl could never understand.) One year he counted all the trees and was pretty sure the original Christmas might have been responsible for reforesting all of Bethlehem.

And he dreaded, almost more than he could bear to describe, the pastor's fateful announcement, inappropriate and alienating, that "Communion is for all those Catholics who are in the state of grace." One year he actually choked while receiving from the communion cup when someone shouted, "Is that like New York or New Jersey?"

It wasn't easy keeping the Christmas spirit as he made his way across the lawn to the rectory just in time to grab a sandwich. The refrigerator, by the pastor's order, would be locked and a sandwich was the best he could hope for. Then shower and prepare for Midnight

Mass.

The place was quiet. The old man wasn't in his usual position in front of the television set doing his regular exercise program – heavy pushdowns. (You mean you don't know about heavy pushdowns? They consist of holding in one hand a TV remote control and pushing down heavily on the buttons during commercial breaks. On an especially boring night one can use up enough calories to easily justify another beer.)

On his bedroom door, however, there was a note, in the pastor's familiar scrawl: "Karl, Not feeling well. Have been battling the flu for a couple of days. Got diarrhea really badly. I'd never make it through the Mass. It's all yours. Sorry. Thanks. Merry Christmas."

It wouldn't have been polite to laugh out loud in the hall; so Karl waited until he was in his room; buried his face in a pillow, and howled hysterically. "Diarrhea! O God, you work in strange ways your wonders to perform. But diarrhea?"

While Karl was settling himself into the euphoria of the moment and realizing that he had nothing prepared for an adult congregation on Christmas Eve (he always got the morning Family Mass), Matt Brock was settling into the bar at Hooligans. He figured he had just over an hour to get well enough schnockered to be able to sit through Monsignor's stories of the "tree shepherd boys" and the "tree Wise Men." God, he had hated it for years.

Mom and Dad insisted, even when he was in college: "It's family, it's tradition; as long as you live in our home, even if you're just visiting, you will go to Mass with us." The first few years of marriage were much the same, except not for the Midnight Mass of the Trees, but morning with the kids. He was tired of Mass.

Then his father suffered a series of strokes and accidents. Christmas changed and Mass became more casual. Father Karl was a missioner on special assignment – doing chaplaincy work at a local prison; his parents were life-long friends of Matt's dad, to whom he had been bringing communion every Sunday for four years, ever since his initial hospitalization. He would arrive around noon and set up on the swimming pool patio of his folks' home; everyone would just be wearing shorts with the kids running around playing with the dog. Because of Dad's condition, the priest made it quick and simple; his dad received communion, and so did the rest of the family. So did Matt, but mostly just to please his father.

Those were strange moments. His father really loved the priest but during those first few communion calls would get so upset when he was told, "Take the Body of Christ in your hands. If you can hold your wife with our hands, if you can hold your children and grandchildren with them, you can hold the Son of God." Eventually, his father just accepted, but it was more than accepting. He would hold the host in his hands and stare, long, gently. It was as if his ruddy Irish complexion would pale, become smoother, gentler. Then, having lifted the bread to his mouth and inhaled it, he would settle peacefully into himself. Quiet, Deep Peace. Deep, Quiet Peace. It was strange. Matt would watch his father and then turn to his mother. She just stared at her husband, seemingly not understanding the transformation but now so accustomed to witnessing it that the vision brought a simple Quiet, Deep Peace to her.

All that was over now. A lot was over. His father died two years ago; his mother moved with his brother to Tallahassee, and Matt's wife Kathy, who wouldn't put up with Matt's drinking any longer, had filed for divorce. She and the kids stayed in the home; he moved out. (Perhaps they might be at Mass this evening — it was a social event for her; everyone from the old neighborhood would show up for what had become almost a block party after Mass.)

For now, he knew why he was sitting at Holligan's. He was going to get schnockered, but he still couldn't figure out why he was planning on making Mass.

"What can I get for you?" the bartender asked.

"Make it a Coors Light," Matt started, suddenly changing to say, "Nah, give me an O'Doul's — what the hell? I haven't had a drink in eight months. Why start now? Geez, this'll be my first sober Christmas in one hell of a long time," he half said/half thought. He was barely finished with his O'Doul's when he decided, "Don't want to show up for Mass with beer on my breath. I'll just get out of here, roll back the moon roof, breeze over to Key Biscayne, air out my head, and then a clean cut down Old Cutler and I'll be right on time."

Father Karl and Matt almost collided while they headed through the front door of the church. Matt wondered, "What am I doing here? I haven't been to confession in years. Communion?" Karl told himself, "I still don't have a sermon. I'll just use *The Story of the Littlest Angel*. Can't go wrong with that."

The Mass began well. If nothing else, the choir was magnificent. Karl was prayerful. Matt was confused. Karl couldn't help continually laughing to himself "diarrhea." Matt felt uncomfortable when he realized that Kathy and the kids were at the end of the pew three rows ahead of him. Karl felt pretty confident when. after the Gospel, he asked all of the children in the congregation to join him sitting on the sanctuary floor. As he prepared to read the story of *The Littlest Angel*, he had an almost uncontrollable urge to throw in a few references to the "tree Wise Men." He resisted. Matt was impressed.

It was a great setting – just right for Christmas. And Matt's two boys looked so good sitting up there with all the other kids.

Karl was pleased. It went well. The kids seemed to like it; parents kept popping up to sneak photos. But, when he was finished, there was still a feeling of something not-quite-right. Excusing himself from the children, he explained that there was something he wanted to say to their parents.

"You know," he began, "I've always heard 'Christmas is for the children,' and 'Christmas is about God's gift of His Son to us.' But, I've been thinking: Wouldn't that be mean-hearted and short-sighted of God — to give a few people the gift of Christ just for a short thirty-three years and then to leave the rest of us with nothing but someone else's memories?

"No. I don't believe that Christmas was simply God's gift of His Son to us. I believe Christmas was a preparation — it was the outside wrapping and ribbons — the Advent — for Holy Thursday. For God's gift of the Christ not just for the moment but for all ages. Christmas is the Advent of Holy Thursday and the Eucharist, Communion. When we take that little piece of bread into our hands, we take the Babe of Bethlehem, the Carpenter, the Fisherman of Galilee, the Teacher from Jerusalem, the Christ of the Cross, and the Messiah of the Resurrection — we take Him into our hands, consecrating them and making them holy; when we take that simple bread into ourselves, we take in the Christ and make ourselves holy in our union — our Communion — with Him.

"Y'all came to the Midnight Mass of Christmas – to celebrate with the Church God's gift of His Son to the world. I hope y'all will come to communion tonight – so that your Christmas celebration will be complete."

The children stayed in the sanctuary throughout the Eucharist. Their presence added a special sense. When, after the Lamb of God prayers, Karl elevated the chalice and paten, he proclaimed, "This is the Christ of Christmas. As He came to the stable that He might – by the mystery of His birth – consecrate our humanity, He comes now to each and all of you. In bread and wine, in communion, to be with you, in you, to be in union with you. This is your communion. This is your Christmas."

With that, joined by the Eucharistic ministers, he moved to begin the distribution of Communion.

Matt sat quietly. He had missed most of the Mass – lost in thought from the end of the priest's impromptu post-sermon comments. Christmas is the Advent of Holy Thursday – that Christ might come to us. In his mind, he could clearly see the changes in his father's face each time he had taken the Christ of Communion in his hands, into his heart.

"I wonder," Matt mused, "does God really worry about how long it's been since my last confession? Does God really worry about how long it's been since the last time I went to Mass? Naaaaaaaaaaaaahhhhhhh!

"Okay, Dad," he said so loudly that the lady in the

342

pew in front of him actually turned around. "This one's for you."

As Karl placed the bread in Matt's hand, as Matt first looked long and hard and then took the same bread in, he prayed, "Lord, be for me just a little of what you were for my dad."

Back in his place, Matt felt peace. Quiet, Deep Peace. Nothing had really changed. He was just there. Nothing had changed. Quiet, Deep Peace. No big deal, no great change. Well….

Matt was almost unaware as Mass came to an end. He did not get caught-up in the great exodus as people rushed for the doors. Eventually, he joined the "front doors block party," met old neighbors and classmates, kissed a few wives, shook hands with growing kids. Then, a small hand slid into his. "Daddy," his older son, Jimmy, now all of seven, was telling him, "Mom says that, if you are sober and you want to, you can come home for Christmas with us."

Karl did not hear the conversation as he watched Matt and his family walk down the long steps ahead of him. By now the church had been locked and people were slowly drifting through the parking lot. He was feeling, well, pretty good. It had been a good liturgy. He enjoyed it. There was a sense of Quiet, Deep Peace. The liturgy, the whole evening, had convinced him that Christmas really was for and about Holy Thursday, about Eucharist, that

Christmas is for Communion.

Now, crossing the expanse of grass between church and rectory, he looked up into the clear star-lit night sky and breathed a quiet "Thanks, God. It's been good." Looking ahead, again, he spotted the darkened rectory. "It's been good, Lord. Thanks. But, Lord, diarrhea…?"

$\mathcal{A}$ Gift From Saints and Martyrs

As we celebrate again the most wonder-inspiring moment of history — the Feast of the Incarnation — God's eternal choice to consecrate and make holy our Humanity in the person of His Son, our Brother and Lord, my mind is filled with the words "broken" and "wounded" and "soul."

I tried. I've genuinely, desperately, hope-filledly, anxiously tried to create a Mikey story for this evening. But, it would not, it could not come. I reflected on, thought about the experiences, the struggles, the adventures and disappointments of the past year and asked myself over and over again how to make sense of them in Mikey's life and mine. But the inspiration would not come.

And so, I will share with you small gifts, a few simple thoughts – some my own, others of saints whom I have known or who lived centuries ago.

◄◦► ◄◦► ◄◦► ◄◦► ◄◦► ◄◦► ◄◦► ◄◦► ◄◦► ◄◦► ◄◦►

Somewhere around eight-hundred-and-fifty years ago, the German Benedictine nun Hildegard of Bingen told us "The mystery of God hugs you in its all-embracing arms." Wow! What an incredible idea. In the Prophet Isaiah, God assures his people of the depth of his love – "Behold, I have carved you into the palm of my hand."

The Eternal God not only hugs us, He cradles us in the palm of His hand. And He whispers gently over and over again into the hearts of each of us how much He loves us. He invites us, calls us, begs us desperately to see ourselves as He does, to stop demanding perfection of ourselves, to live without undue guilt and life-destroying shame. He calls us to nurture our souls – not with pious practices but with beach walks and blooming orchid plants, with walking slowly in the rain and through – not around or over – rain puddles; to play air guitar with wild, reckless abandon and for pure joy; daring to go barefoot in wet grass "just because...." To be silent in the depths of night and celebrate the sleeping breaths of our children or those whom we love. To turn off the TV and read a truly good book. To laugh – heartily and out loud at a good joke or simply because we allow ourselves to enjoy a memory and then laugh out loud again because it puts a puzzled look on people's faces when they can't figure out why your laughing.

◄O►◄O►◄O►◄O►◄O►◄O►◄O►◄O►◄O►◄O►◄O►

My friend – the Saint and Martyr – Maryknoll Sister Carla Piette wrote:

> *The Lord has guided me so far and in his guidance he has up and dropped me here... at this time and in this place in history, to search for and find him.*
> *Not somewhere else. But here.*
> *And so HERE I WILL STAY, until I have found that broken Lord*
> *in all his forms and all his various pieces, until I have completely bound-up his wounds*
> *and covered his whole body,*
> *his people with the rich oil of gladness.*
> *And when that has been done, he will up and drop me again –*

either into his promised kingdom or into the midst
or another jigsaw puzzle of his broken body,
his hurting people.

What an incredibly, magically consoling idea: In an age and time when so many are broken, wounded and hurting, He who is called Emmanuel — God With Us — wishes that each of us be right where we are and that we know that God Is With Us — we need only to "search for and find Him... in all his forms and all his various pieces..." and to share with them — His People — "the rich oil of God's gladness." What a wonderful idea: that we are where God has dropped us.

◄◦►◄◦►◄◦►◄◦►◄◦►◄◦►◄◦►◄◦►◄◦►◄◦►◄◦►

My friend — Saint and Martyr — Maryknoll Sister Ita Ford: wrote to her niece on the occasion of her sixteenth birthday:

"...[S]ome things hold true wherever one is, and at whatever age. What I'm saying is, I hope you come to find that which gives life a deep meaning for you...something worth living for, maybe even worth dying for...something that energizes you, enthuses you, enables you to keep moving ahead. I can't tell you what it might be — that's for you to find, to choose, to love.

I can just encourage you to start looking, and support you in the search.

"I want to say to you: don't waste the gifts and opportunities you have to make yourself and other people happy... I hope this doesn't sound like some kind of a sermon because I don't mean it that way. Rather, it's something you learn here (in El Salvador, where she was martyred), and I want to share it with you. In fact, it's my birthday present to you. If it doesn't make sense right at this moment, keep this and read it sometime from now. Maybe it will be clearer..."

Today we celebrate something worth living for, something worth dying for – that God so loves us, just as we are, without perfection, filled with flaws, overcome sometimes by our woundedness, by our brokenness – but made in His image and made holy by the mysteries of Christmas and hugged by His all-embracing arms.

Let us pray that the Angel's message – "Today is born our Savior, Christ the Lord" – energizes us, enables us to keep moving ahead – wherever "ahead" may be. Let us find it – our Unknown, let use chose it, let us love it – our Unknown. Let us begin looking and, in our search, let us encourage and support each other.

𝔐erry 𝔠hristmas

GRATITUDE

This collection of Christmas gifts
is dedicated to my family:
my parents, Frank and Mary;
brothers and sister, Barry, Michael and Colleen,
and my nephew, Blaine Gordon Butcher.

By opening their home to
hundreds and hundreds of people
over decades of Christmas Eves, they reflected the
hospitality of the Stable.
I am forever grateful.

Story telling is more ancient than the Judeo-Christian Scriptures, but it is particularly important to our Faith traditions. I am especially grateful to the People of God and the bilingual "Catholic Christian Community" of Our Lady of Divine Providence Church (Miami), who, more than forty years ago, encouraged me to "keep telling stories."

I remain forever grateful to and for the community of the Maryknoll Missionary Fathers and Brothers (the Catholic Foreign Mission Society of America), who nourished and nurtured my sense of mission as a way of being and allowed me the Grace of Priesthood. For more than fifty years, I have prayed in gratitude for Father (and Surgeon) Scott Harris of Maryknoll, who has encouraged and sustained my vision of mission and service.

To the Sisters of the Maryknoll Contemplative Community — "the Cloister" or "the Chalet," who have supported me in my ministry and life and who appear more than once or twice in these stories, I look forward to continuing to send you ooooey-goooey mangos for many years to come as an expression of my prayerful gratitude.

There are no words with which to express my appreciation for the education I received through the ministry of the Sisters of the Immaculate Heart of Mary of Philadelphia who taught my brothers and sister and me at Epiphany School in South Miami. I continue to fondly remember Sister Charles Borromeo, Sister Marie Anita (who once flunked me in Religion) and Sister Mary Paraclete. While Miguelito and I made fond and kidding references to them, there is no denying that they are the best of the best.

To the inmates, recovering addicts, students at the University of Miami, my friends and students in China, Sigma Chi undergraduates and alumni, and three special Marines – Connor, Tom and Michael: So many of you have given me insights into the Gospel and the Mystery of Christmas for which I am so very thankful.

To Lorie Greenspan and Barry Chesler of TriMark Press for their patience and insight in editing and bringing this gift from rough text to reality, and Chad Thompson for his illustrations, thank you.

This collection of Christmas gifts would never have been possible without the generosity of Michael and Susan and Gabe Lewis-Keister and Al and Marty Babbington and their In-the-Room-In-the-Deal Entertainment. The publication of these stories is a reflection of your kindness and generosity. Thank you! Michael,... I lack the words. It's been a long road. I look forward to our next adventures.

To each of you – unnamed friends who inspired them and friends named in these stories and friends with whom I have shared them through the years, I can only echo the heartfelt words of St. Paul: "I give thanks to the Lord, my God, for you every day of my life."

THE ST. FRANCIS TAU

The last letter of the Hebrew alphabet, the Tau, was used symbolically in the Old Testament to signify the faithful servants of God. "The Lord said to him, 'Go through the city, through Jerusalem, and mark a Tau upon the foreheads of the men who sigh and groan over the 'abominations' " of their time. (Ezekiel 9:4) The Tau symbolized their goodness and protected them from the destruction that was to come.

Early Christians adopted the Tau for two reasons: It prophesied the Last Day and served as a reminder of the Cross of Christ. With its resemblance to the Cross, the Tau was especially dear to St. Francis of Assisi – the sign of his deep spiritual conviction that the salvation of every man and woman is in the Cross of Christ.

It is probable that Francis heard Pope Innocent III's exhortation at the opening of the Fourth Lateran Council (1215): "We are called to reform our lives, to stand in the presence of God as righteous people. God will know us by the sign of the Tau, marked on our forehead."

For St. Francis, the Tau represented lifelong fidelity to the Cross of Jesus and a reflection of Francis' pledge to serve the least – the poorest of the poor. Thomas of Celano, one of Francis' first companions and his first biographer, told us, "Francis preferred the Tau above all other symbols; he utilized it as his only signature for his letters and he painted the image of it on the walls of all the places he stayed." Another early biographer, St. Bonaventure, noted that Francis "traced it on himself before beginning each of his actions."

Bonaventure recounted that in 1223, three years before his death, St. Francis, who was a deacon, visited the mountainside town of Greccio. Recognizing that the chapel of the Franciscan hermitage would be too small for the congregation for Midnight Mass, he established an altar near the town square and constructed the first Christmas creche.

"He prepared a manger, and brought hay, and an ox and an ass to the place appointed. The brethren were summoned, the people ran together, the forest resounded with their voices, and that venerable night was made glorious by many and brilliant lights and sonorous psalms of praise... The man of God [St. Francis] stood before the manger, full of devotion and piety, bathed in tears and radiant with joy; the Holy Gospel was chanted by Francis... Then he preached to the people around the nativity of the poor King; and being unable to utter His name for the tenderness of His love, He called Him the Babe of Bethlehem... [There was] an infant marvelously beautiful sleeping in the manger, Whom the blessed Father Francis embraced with both his arms, as if he would awake Him from sleep...." [Local legend has it that, when St. Francis held the statue of the Child Jesus, it miraculously sprang to life.]

Francis' creche was prepared in a cave; two living creatures — an ox and an ass; no Mary, no Joseph. Simplicity itself. A simple story.

In the spirit of St. Francis, we have placed the Tau at the bottom of each page. In the spirit of St. Francis, we pray that these little gifts — these simple stories — find a place in your hearts and help you grow in the Joy and Wonder of Christmas.